CRUSTACEANS

Ann Arbor
Science
Library

CRUSTACEANS

by Waldo L. Schmitt

ANN ARBOR

THE UNIVERSITY OF MICHIGAN PRESS

Preface

It is not now, nor will it ever be given to one man to observe all the things recounted in the following pages. Though some of the information is drawn from personal experience both in the field and laboratory, for a very great deal I am indebted to other students of Crustacea.

Dr. Mary J. Rathbun (1860-1943), dean of the American carcinologists of her day, for me, stands first among them. It was Miss Rathbun who first introduced me to the Crustacea and it was from her that I learned most of what I know of their systematics and taxonomy, and of the wealth of literature devoted to them.

I am beholden also to the Rev. T. R. R. Stebbing (1835-1926) for his *History of Crustacea* (1893), and to Dr. W. T. Calman (1871-1952) for his *Life of Crustacea* (1911), works which originally inspired me to undertake this somewhat similar attempt. To the very generous patrons of science who made possible a number of my more recent collecting expeditions to places far and near—Huntington Hartford of New York, J. Bruce and Mrs. Bredin of Wilmington, Delaware, Captain Allan Hancock of Los Angeles and Santa Maria, California, and President Franklin D. Roosevelt (1882-1945)—I am especially grateful. I would be remiss should I fail to mention, also, several goodwill missions to Latin America for our Department of State during the war years, and the never-to-be-forgotten austral summer (1962-63) spent in Antarctica under the auspices of the United States Antarctic Program of the National Science Foundation and the Arctic Institute of North America.

Furthermore, I am indebted to the editors and authors of the several sections on Crustacea (1926-27) in the Kukenthal (Willy)- Krumbach (Thilo) *Handbuch der Zoologie*, and of the *Physiology of Crustacea* (Talbot H. Waterman, editor, 1960-61); to the late Mrs. Isabel M. Lewis of the U. S. Naval Observatory for references to constellation lore, and to Mr. Watson Boyes of the Oriental Institute of the University of Chicago for historical information relating to the Crustacea known to the ancients; and for vastly more than can here be acknowledged to the various scientific institutions and U.S. Government agencies with which I have served at one time or another: the Fish and Wildlife Service (formerly Bureau of Fisheries), the Carnegie Institution of Washington, the Smithsonian Institution, and the Walter Rathbone Bacon Scholarship, and above all to the United States National Museum for its support, laboratory facilities, and opportunities afforded for learning, at first-hand, much of what I know of Crustacea.

The classification herein adopted is based on recent studies concerned with the relationships, morphology, and physiology of the Class Crustacea, particularly Rolf Siewing's "Studies in Malacostracan Morphology," a special publication of the Museum of Comparative Zoology, Harvard University, 1963.

Beyond the foregoing acknowledgments and those made elsewhere in the accompanying text, I wish to express my appreciation for the critical and very helpful reading given the manuscript of this revised text by Drs. Fenner A. Chace, Jr., and Horton H. Hobbs, Jr., colleagues and senior scientists on the National Museum's staff of the Department of Invertebrate Zoology.

Crustaceans was first published in 1931 in the now long out of print Smithsonian Scientific Series (vol. 10). The accomplishment of this revised text is due wholly to the interest taken in it by The University of Michigan Press.

Without the *Zoological Record*, that comprehensive annual index to the literature of zoology published by the Zoological Society of London, this book could never have been written.

Smithsonian Institution   Waldo L. Schmitt
Washington, 1965

Contents

Even from the Shrimps to the Leviathan
Enquiry ran.

—Thomas Heyward
Searching for God

Introduction

My first thought in undertaking this work was, How little man knows of crustaceans, of their significance in the economy of nature as a whole and to himself in particular! Most of us have some personal knowledge of their value as food, but few are aware of the many other ways in which they serve or disserve mankind. Crustaceans may be serious pests: some cause the destruction of crops; others, in oriental and tropical countries, are widespread carriers of disease; ships must be on guard against certain of them or lose in the race for speed and expedition of valuable cargoes; if unmolested, boring Crustacea will destroy expensive wharves and harbor works of wood, undermine sea walls and even bore into stone dock facings, and some go so far as to put submarine cables out of commission. The variety of their habitats is even more startling. They inhabit most of the waters on the earth—both salt and fresh—the icy waters of the polar regions, the hot waters of thermal springs, the waters of high mountains and those of the ocean's great abysses. Some live in little plant-formed pockets of water high in the tops of trees; others live in rock; and a multitude are parasites, living in and on practically all other classes of animals.

But even an acquaintance with these random facts about crustaceans leaves us still ignorant of their vital zoological importance. Vast hordes of certain kinds are at the base of the pyramid of aquatic life. Remove them, and most of the other aquatic creatures will perish, for crustaceans are the main food animals of the waters. Certain species subsist to a larger extent than any other animals on the microscopic vegetable life of the sea—chiefly diatoms. Transmuting this relatively inaccessible food supply into their own minute forms of life, these species in turn become the food of many fishes and other animals. The world's largest living animals, the blue whales—which may measure a hundred feet in length and weigh a hundred tons—as well as the tiny, transparent fish fry—so small that one could hold a hundred in one hand—depend chiefly upon small crustaceans for their food supply. To play so large a part in zoological economy, crustaceans must exist in unbelievable numbers.

Creatures of such unsuspected importance and numbers stir our imagination and invite us to find out more about them. But let us beware of lightly following our curiosity in this matter. The attempt to obtain a clear-cut definition of the class Crustacea has left many a student bewildered and dissatisfied. The crustaceans are too numerous, too complex, too remote in their characteristics from the animals with which we are more instinctively familiar for us to form a concept of them which will remain as distinct in our minds as the concept of mammals is from that of birds.

All mammals secrete milk with which they nourish their young, and all birds have feathers; but crustaceans do not seem to have any single unifying character—that is, no character which is common to all the members of the class and which would single out every member from the members of all other classes of animals. The name Crustacea, derived from the Latin word for shell, would imply that the animals so christened are shelled creatures. The crabs, shrimps, and crayfishes—the members of this class most familiar to us—have shells of a kind, of course; but many other members in perfectly good standing do not.

In a very general way we might describe crustaceans as the water-breathing "insects" of the sea. The two classes Insecta and Crustacea are probably descendants of a common ancestor and they belong in the same major division of the animal kingdom, the Arthropoda—animals with jointed feet. But such a description accomplishes little toward enabling the casual observer to recognize a crustacean on sight, especially if he met one, as he is very apt to do, on land.

In the absence, then, of anything more explicit and helpful, our definition must resort to such negative and alternative characters as—to quote T. R. R. Stebbing—"that the division of the Arthropoda called Crustacea have a segmented body and limbs at some stage of life; that either they have gills or else they breathe in water through their skins; that they have no proper neck; that they never have wings; and that they are born in locomotive freedom. Like insects, they have an integument or cuticle composed of a substance called chitin. This may be extremely flexible, or, passing through various degrees of tough and brittle, may, by the copious addition of chalky material, attain the hardness of bone or brick." But unlike insects, Crustacea typically have two pairs of feelers, or antennae, whereas the insects and their nearer relatives have but a single pair. This is perhaps the salient character distinguishing the one group from the other.

We can see at once that these various affirmations and negations apply to crab, shrimp, and lobster. They apply also to barnacles, which, though they are generally met with in permanent attachment to ships' bottoms, pilings, or rocks, are born with the ability to move about freely. They apply also to some of those aquatic animals commonly called water-fleas, fish-lice, and hermit crabs. Of the animals met with in our cellars and gardens, they apply to the wood lice, including sow-bugs and pill-bugs.

The foregoing comprise a very few—the best known—of the twenty thousand-odd kinds or species of animals which our definition brings under the heading Crustacea. Man has no popular name for the vast remainder. They make no direct appeal to his pleasure or convenience; mostly they live their lives beyond the realm of his physical experience; hence he tends to ignore them.

Man's acquaintance with the few members of the class that he does recognize, however, goes far back—indefinitely farther than the beginnings of written history. Early, man—perhaps the Babylonians sometime about 2100 B.C.—translated the crab to the heavens, putting it in the zodiac as the sign of the constellation *Cancer*, which is the Latin word for crab (Fig. 1). On every map of the northern hemisphere of sufficient scale is noted the "Tropic of Cancer": Tropic, from the Greek for the turn or change which marks the most northern limit on the earth's surface at which the sun may be directly overhead and at which the sun seems to pause before

FIG. 1. The constellation Cancer with the crab *Potamon*, as probably visualized in the sky by the Babylonians.

retracing its course to the south; and Cancer from our "crab" constellation. It is when entering this constellation that the sun is said to be at its summer solstice— the point in its apparent path at which the sun is farthest from the equator, in northern latitudes. The crab constellation is also called the "dark" constellation and is supposed to represent the powers of darkness. A little clay tablet dating back to 500 B.C., dug up in the valley of the Euphrates, gives us an unmistakable clue to the crab the Babylonians had in mind. Graven on the tablet in cuneiform characters is the statement that the crab appears as the constellation of the fourth month, under the name of *Nagar-assura*. *Nagar-assura* means the "workman-of-the-river-bed," a description as accurate as it is poetic of the genus *Potamon*—the common fresh-water crab, represented by one or two exceedingly closely related species that occur throughout all the Mediterranean watershed and islands, and from thence eastward into Mesopotamia and southward into Egypt and the Sahara.

These common crabs, which were eaten by all the early peoples of this region as they are by the peoples there today, live in burrows along the swamps and water courses. What more suggestive of darkness than the dank burrows in the river mud which the crab excavates downward, in the general direction, at least, of the bowels of the earth?

The familiarity of the ancient Mediterranean peoples with *Potamon* is further evidenced to us by their coins (Fig. 2), some of which bear unmistakable impressions of this "workman-of-the-river-bed." This use of Crustacea —particularly crabs, shrimps, lobsters, and crayfish—on coinage, was widespread in the Phoenician and Greek settlements. Ancient Akragas—modern Agrigento, on the south coast of Sicily—took the crab as its emblem. Many very beautiful coins from Akragas, all bearing the same crab (*Potamon edulis*) are preserved to us.

One of the coins of Phaistos, among the oldest of the

FIG. 2. Crustaceans on ancient coins (1-3) and gem stones (4-5). From various authors.

Cretan cities, shows Hercules with a lion skin over his arm striking at the Hydra with a club, while between his feet is the crab which nipped him at Juno's behest and which, after the hero had crushed it, the goddess raised to a place among the stars as a reward. It is thus that the Greeks explained to their own satisfaction the origin of the constellation *Cancer*.

There are pictorial representations of crustaceans that probably antedate their use on coins. In Egypt the expedition under the auspices of Queen Hatshepsut of the XVIIIth dynasty (1580-1350 B.C.) to Punt, on the Red Sea, recorded among other things the different types of fish and some of the crustaceans found. These were drawn on the wall of her temple at Deir-el-Bahri (Fig. 3).

Other very old representations of Crustacea indicative of considerable knowledge of the class are those which were done in relief, along with representations of fish, on the walls of the palace of Sennacherib, ruler of Assyria from 705-681 B.C. (Fig. 4). Fragments of these are still in existence.

FIG. 3. Wall decoration in the temple at Deir el-Bahri, recording finds of an Egyptian expedition to Punt, on the Red Sea, about 1500 B.C. The lobster is believed to be *Panulirus penicillatus.* Courtesy of the Oriental Institute, The University of Chicago.

FIG. 4. Assyrian wall relief showing conquest of tribes inhabiting marshes of the Euphrates. Note crabs in the water. After Patterson.

The scientific study of Crustacea, as indeed of all natural history, begins with Aristotle. As he himself expressed it, "I found no basis prepared; no models to copy.... Mine is the first step, and therefore a small one, though worked out with much thought and hard labor. It must be looked at as a first step and judged with indulgence. You, my readers, or hearers of my lectures, if you think I have done as much as can fairly be required for an initiatory start, as compared with more advanced departments of theory, will acknowledge what I have achieved and pardon what I have left for others to accomplish."

The completeness of Aristotle's description of certain Crustacea is well-nigh recent in treatment, and nearly a dozen species can be surely identified from his data, while another six are doubtfully placed. The total exceeds that of all the species we have been able to trace from all other records of the ancient world.

From Aristotle to Linnaeus, a period of nearly twenty-one hundred years, the contributors to carcinology (the study of Crustacea), good and bad, numbered less than half a hundred. In this vast span of years one can trace the evolution of the subject—barring the direct observations of Aristotle—from mere fancy, fabrication, and conjecture through observation, study, and some experimentation to the orderly classification of specimens and material as achieved by Linnaeus, who introduced the binomial naming of animals by genus and species and brought order out of chaos.

With the publication of the tenth edition of Linnaeus' *Systema Naturae* in 1758—a date to be remembered as the nativity, to all intents and purposes, of systematic zoology—carcinology took on the status of a science. Its development has gathered momentum with the years, and an indication of its present scope is to be found in the *Zoological Record* (London), which listed during the first sixty years of this century over twenty-five thousand publications concerned with Crustacea, recent and fossil.

I. Body Organization and Functions

From the giant crab of Japan (Fig. 5), which may span twelve feet between the tips of its outstretched claws, crustaceans scale down in size to water-fleas and copepods so minute that only a powerful microscope can reveal for us their make-up and enable us to distinguish between their kinds. The edible crabs, shrimps, and lobsters, with which most of us are familiar, all belong to the most highly developed members of the class, the order Decapoda, or ten-footed crustaceans. Perhaps if we appeal to these more familiar animals for a general introduction to the habits and structure of Crustacea, we shall realize that they have to accomplish the same fundamental processes to sustain life as does the human organism, and that the mechanisms they have evolved in many aspects are strikingly similar to ours. If we get on terms of intimacy with the higher Crustacea, the subsequent introduction to their more reclusive relatives will prove less of an ordeal.

The Decapoda constitute a well-defined order of Crustacea in spite of the great diversity of form exhibited by their members. Superficially a crab seems to bear little

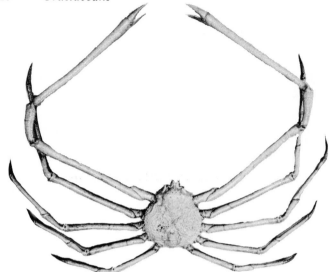

FIG. 5. Specimen of the giant spider crab (*Macrocheira kaempferi*) of Japan. Courtesy of the U.S. National Museum.

resemblance to a lobster or shrimp. Yet if you examine closely any of the edible crabs that come to your table you will be surprised at how lobsterlike they are in structure. A casual inspection will reveal some common characters which will enable you to distinguish the Decapoda from the rest of the crustaceans.

Our definition of Crustacea began with the statement that all the members of this class have at some time in their lives a segmented body. We might, as a matter of fact, project on the screen of our imagination an idealized simplification of the ancestral crustacean, which would consist of a series of simple rings, each with a pair of appendages; something, for example, like the rattles of a rattlesnake armed with legs. And back to such a simplified norm we might reduce all the complex variations of form and structure now exhibited by the thousands of known species of Crustacea: of so elemental a nature is segmentation in this class of animals. Insects have it, too, however, so that we cannot use it as the sole delimiting character of Crustacea.

The factor that calls attention to the segmentation of the shrimp or lobster body is the hard shell covering of each ring or somite. Such shelly rings (Fig. 6) overlap and make an external skeleton—exoskeleton—for the crustacean like a suit of jointed armor, headpiece and all. But, though jointed, the rings are really continuous over the entire body, including the limbs. This body covering or cuticle is made of a chitin-protein substance (from here on referred to simply as chitin). At the joints it is thin and soft, permitting the parts to move upon one another, but elsewhere it is hardened by the deposition of carbonate and other salts of lime. Though the somites can move backwards and forwards upon one another they cannot move laterally, because the soft joints are interrupted at the sides by interlocking hinge joints—a fact which prevents a lobster from swimming in any other direction than forward or backward.

FIG. 6. Abdominal ring of a lobster with its appendages.

The first things to look at, then, in a proper considera-
tion of the relationships of a decapod are its body
segments or somites. We are rather apt to think of a
crab as covered by a single shell or carapace, like a
turtle. That, however, is because of the deceptive, great
development of the dorsum of a single somite—the one
carrying the jaws or mandibles. The other somites are
present, also; but they are hidden under their overgrown
comrade, as you will see by turning the crab over on his
back.

The number of segments is an important character
which distinguishes the true Malacostraca—the great
subclass to which the order Decapoda belongs—from all
other crustaceans. Invariably in the true Malacostraca
the body is divided into nineteen segments, although
sometimes two or more somites will be partially or
completely fused. But the existence of a segment can
often be determined by the appendages, of which every
somite originally had one pair and only one pair. Thus
where two or more pairs of appendages appear to be
attached to but a single segment, one can be certain
that fusion has taken place.

Nearly all of the nineteen somites can be seen in a
more or less completely segmented malacostracan like
Anaspides (see Fig. 33). In our lobster, shrimp, or crab
the whole nineteen can generally be counted out by
appendages, imperfect fusion, or by comparison with
related genera in which fusion has not taken place.

There are two sections of the crustacean body which
are generally not considered true somites. At the head
this excluded portion is that which bears the eyes.
Because of their manner of development these important
sense organs are generally not classed as appendages,
and therefore the section bearing them is not a somite
in the true sense of the word. At the other extremity the
section not admitted to the rank of a true segment is the
tailpiece, or telson, which is always devoid of appendages.

So restricted, we have in the Malacostraca nineteen true, typical, appendage-bearing somites, not including the eye-bearing portion of the body and the telson. The number is constant and serves as a basic character for the classification of the group.

A glance at Figure 7 will show better than a volume of words what a typical decapod—a shrimp—looks like. The body is divided into three main regions—head, thorax, and abdomen. The head and the thorax are coalesced and covered by a dorsal outgrowth of the mandibular segment, which forms a dorsal shield technically known as the carapace.

If the shrimp had a neck it would be much simpler to understand why the first five segments—Nos. 1 to 5—are called the head. But at least they occur at the proper end of the creature and carry many of the sense organs. These segments are fused, but we can see that there were five of them originally by counting the appendages. The first two pairs of appendages are the crustacean's feelers, called respectively the first antennae, or antennules, and the second antennae, or antennae proper. In nauplii and typically uniramous, the antennules are biramous in Malacostraca. The third pair of appendages are the mandibles, or jaws proper; while the fourth and fifth pairs are the accessory jaws, called maxillae or sometimes (if designated separately), the maxillula and maxilla, respectively.

The next eight segments—Nos. 6 to 13, inclusive—make up the thorax. As an indication of the arbitrary division between thorax and head, we find that the first three pairs of appendages in this section are comparable to the last two of the head; that is, they, also, are accessory jaws, called maxillipeds (jaw feet).

The five segments numbered 9, 10, 11, 12, and 13 carry the five pairs of legs from which the Decapoda derive their ordinal name.

The abdomen, with six somites, brings the total number of somites in the shrimp to the specified nineteen

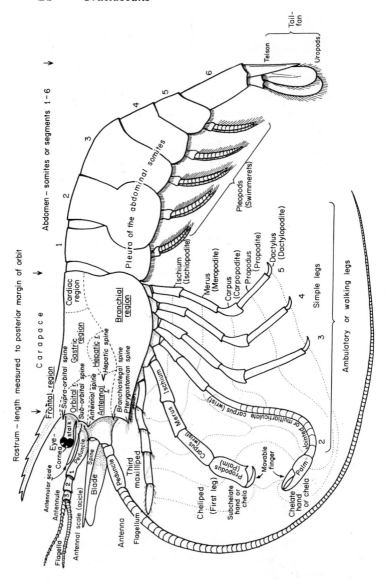

FIG. 7. Conventionalized shrimp, illustrating terms used in the description and classification of crustaceans.

characteristic of a typical malacostracan. Appendage pairs Nos. 14, 15, 16, 17, and 18 are the pleopods, or swimmerets. The last, or 19th, pair of appendages consists of the uropods, which when present constitute, with the telson, the tail-fan. The telson is, of course, part of the abdomen, though not of true somitic rank.

We are apt to think of the crab as without a tail. This does it an injustice; for though flexed and flattened and practically devoid of meat, a normal abdomen or tail is present (Fig. 8).

So much for the number and arrangement of our crustacean's appendages. It may increase our respect for the appendages to learn something of their variety of form and function.

The mandibles, which most resemble teeth in some crustaceans, serve to cut up such pieces of food as may be presented them by the other mouth appendages.

The ten pairs of appendages which follow the mandibles—Nos. 4 to 13, inclusive, in the true Malacostraca —have more or less generally allotted to them, to quote Stebbing, the functions of "tasting and pasting, biting and fighting, grasping and clasping, walking and a kind of inarticulate talking, swimming, burrowing, house building, besides the automatic services which they render to the eggs in the brood pouch and to the animal's own respiration."

To match such diversity of function we may rightly expect some diversity of form in these appendages. Some, in fact, are a kind of jaws—organs of the mouth— while others are a kind of arms or legs—organs of the trunk. But whatever their function or form, all appendages, from antennules to uropods, seem to be reducible to a common pattern consisting of a stem and two branches—one inner and the other outer. The inner is the main branch of the appendage, and the outer is often left rather primitively flagelliform or lashlike.

Both stem and branches are jointed. Three joints are theoretically the normal number for the stem or peduncle; usually there are but two, or more rarely only one.

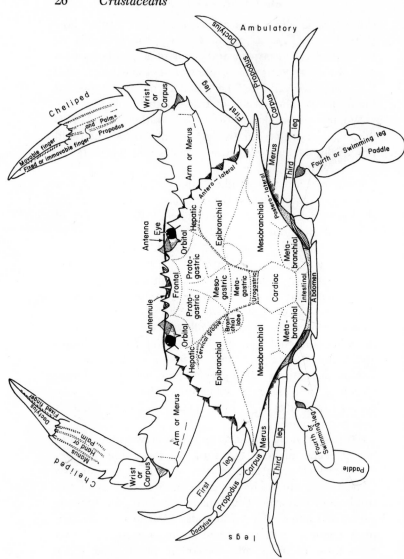

FIG. 8a. Diagram of edible blue crab (*Callinectes sapidus*), illustrating terms used in description and classification of decapod crustaceans. Dorsal view. After Rathbun.

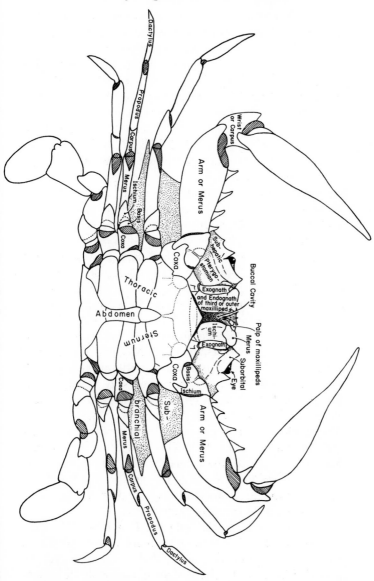

FIG. 8b. Ventral view of edible blue crab.

The number of joints in the branches may vary considerably, five being a normal number for the inner branch of the appendages of the head and thorax.

With so many units to work with, it is no wonder that a decapod crustacean will have available almost any tool it needs. To make pincers, for instance, the only thing it needs to do is to draw out one joint beyond the point where the next is attached to it. This is how the great crushing claw, or chela, of a crab or lobster is made. Whenever an appendage develops a pincer or chela it is said to be chelate.

Often where an appendage is used as an oar both branches are developed and composed of many joints, each furnished with a fringe of hairs (Fig. 9, No. 1), so that the whole makes an effective swimming organ.

A crustacean can cast off a limb and grow a new one in its place. This provision serves it in good stead as a means of escape from enemies. Such a voluntary break in the lobster's appendages occurs at a "fracture plane" in the second joint of the limb (basis, Fig. 8b) where in lobster and crab-like decapods it is immovably fused with the third (the ischium). At this point the internal cavity is crossed by a transverse partition with a small opening through which the nerves and blood vessels pass, but not the muscles of the leg. The lobster produces the break by a spasmodic contraction of these muscles. The partition facilitates the formation of a blood clot and this stops the bleeding. The growing of a new limb begins at once with the formation of a bud beneath the scar left by the breaking off of the old one. The bud takes on the shape of a limb, ordinarily after a few molts indistinguishable from its predecessor.

Thus we come to the subject of molting. We have pointed out that the decapod is completely inclosed in a more or less continuous hard-shelled covering hinged like a suit of armor. This hard shell is incapable of expansion, of course, so in order to find room for an increas-

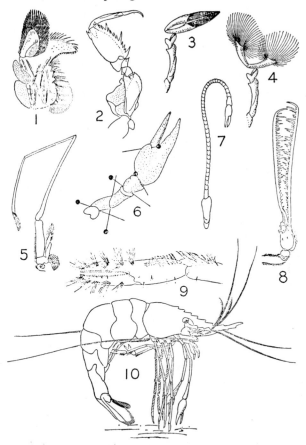

FIG. 9. Diverse appendages. 1, oar foot of a branchiopod; 2, amphipod claw; 3 and 4, closed and open claw of shrimp with brush of hairs for catching small organisms; 5, euphausiid leg; 6, crawfish claw (pins show axes of articulation); 7, multiarticulate shrimp leg; 8, claw of lobsterlike decapod; 9, claw with cleaning brushes; 10, brushes in action.

ing girth the crab, lobster, or shrimp has to shed its housing periodically. It does this by backing out through a transverse slit across the hinder "waist line" of the shell, much as we might withdraw from a one-piece suit through a slit across the small of the back.

The edible blue crab of the Atlantic coast, whose molting has been rather extensively studied, gives warning of an approaching molt several days in advance. A black line appears just within the thin outer and back margins of the outer segments of the swimming legs. This line changes to white and then to red, two or three days before the molt. Fishermen call the crab in this condition a "peeler." At the moment of molting the carapace begins to move away from the abdomen, and a crack appears in each side of the shell, extending almost to the mouth. The posterior part of the body begins to protrude through the gap thus made. At this time the crab usually lies motionless, but it can swim quite actively if disturbed. The remainder of the molting process requires about fifteen minutes. The carapace is lifted higher, the swimming legs begin to be withdrawn by rhythmic throbbing movements, and the body protrudes more and more from the shell (Fig. 10).

When the crab has freed itself completely from its old housing, it is that table delicacy known as a soft-shelled crab. It remains so for a short time only, for within forty-eight hours the new shell has gotten almost too hard to permit of use as a "soft-shell." As a consequence, most of the commercial soft-shelled crabs are caught as peelers and kept in floats until a few hours after molting, when they are marketed. At the time of shedding, the soft, new shell permits of expansion, and a blue crab that measured three and a half inches in width of carapace before a molt may measure four and a half inches four hours afterwards. This rapid increase in size results in large measure from the absorption of water. The hardening of the new shell is due to the deposition of lime salts. Normally, all decapods seem to eat their discarded housings immediately after molting, a habit which may be nature's device for furnishing the large supply of lime salts needed for rapid hardening of the new shell.

FIG. 10. Successive stages in the molting of the edible blue crab.
Courtesy of the U. S. Bureau of Fisheries.

Molting is, of course, an exhausting and dangerous process, and considering the defenselessness of the crustacean while it is going on it must be attended by a high mortality. As one author has stated, molting is the price these animals pay for their protective armor. It is a process for which the epicure at least, may be grateful.

When a malacostracan molts, it sheds the lining of its stomach and the hinder part of its intestinal tract as well as its shell. The linings are continuous with the shell and composed of the same substance, chitin. The stomach, incidentally, is an extraordinary mechanism. It consists of two chambers. The chitinous lining in places is thickened to form a system of plates or "millstones," which by muscular action engage with three strong teeth set in the narrow opening between the two chambers to grind up the food ingested. Quite aptly the apparatus is called the "gastric mill."

The decapod heart lies in the animal's back under the carapace. From it a system of arteries carries the blood to the body tissues. Of veins as we understand them crustaceans have none, but the blood finds its way back to the heart by ill-defined channels which open into the pericardium, or space surrounding the heart. From this it is let into the heart by six valves, which allow its entrance but not its exit.

On its way back to the heart some of the blood passes through the gills, which take the place of the lungs of higher animals. A lobster has twenty gills on each side of the thorax under the carapace. This position insures protection and yet permits a constant supply of water to pass over them. In fact a special plate or "bailer" called the scaphognathite lies in front of the gills and by maintaining a constant motion during life causes a regular stream of water to flow forward over them. Each gill looks much like a feather with thick barbs. The blood streams through the minute channels in the stem and barbs and is separated from the water only by a thin tissue or membrane, which readily permits absorption of oxygen and discharge of carbon dioxide by the blood. The purified blood returns by a series of inner channels to the pericardium and the heart.

The higher crustaceans have more a hint than a reality of a brain in a nerve center in the front of the head that sends nerves to the eyes, antennules, and antennae. The principal part of the nervous system of these creatures is the ventral nerve chain, which runs along the underside of the body and from which nerves lead off at intervals to the various organs and appendages.

All the Decapoda and most other Crustacea reproduce as do vertebrate animals, namely, by the union of the two sexes. The reproductive organs of the decapods are situated in each sex in a comparable position, to either side and just below the heart. The external openings usually occur on or near the basal segments of the last pair of legs in the males, and in the females, the third from last pair. The female often has a special organ, called a sperm-receptacle, between the last pair of legs, wherein she stores the sperm from the male until the eggs are ready to be deposited. In most true Malacostraca the female carries the eggs after extrusion until they are hatched. They are usually cemented in bunches to the swimmerets, and one lobster may carry from three thousand to one hundred thousand eggs (Fig. 11).

The parent crustacean who knew its own child would indeed be wondrous wise, for most young at the time of hatching bear but slight resemblance to the authors—male or female—of their being. In fact some young go through a metamorphosis as extraordinary as the change of a maggot into a fly or of a caterpillar into a moth or butterfly. Often the transformation involves several stages, each strikingly different from the others—so different, in fact, that naturalists of an earlier day were quite understandably deceived into believing that each stage represented a different animal.

Our Decapoda exhibit various degrees of metamorpho-

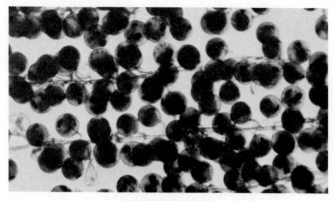

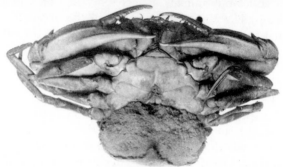

FIG. 11. Female blue crab and eggs. Upper, photomicrograph of eggs attached to hairs of swimmerets (x 120). Lower gravid female. Courtesy of the U.S. Bureau of Fisheries.

sis as well as no metamorphosis at all. The "workman-of-the-river-bed," *Potamon,* the crab that we found elevated to the zodiac by the Babylonians, hatches from the egg as a replica of the adult crab. The common fresh-water crayfish hatches with all the appendages of the adult except the first pair of swimmerets and the uropods. The lobster, though it goes through several larval stages, might still be recognized for what it is when hatched; but no one would dream that the newly hatched porcellanid crab shown in Figure 12 was the offspring of the adult into which it grows.

The simplest form in which any crustacean may hatch from the egg is as a nauplius larva. The nauplius has a tiny, rounded body wholly unsegmented but carrying three pairs of movable appendages: the antennules; the antennae; and the mandibles, or better, mandibular legs. All three pairs of appendages serve to propel the larva through the water.

The nauplius is the link which ties together all crustaceans. It would appear that the nauplius, from its prevalence throughout the Crustacea, was established as a larval form at a period of development prior to the divergence of the existing groups. All crustaceans go through a nauplius stage, either suppressed within the egg or as the first stage after hatching.

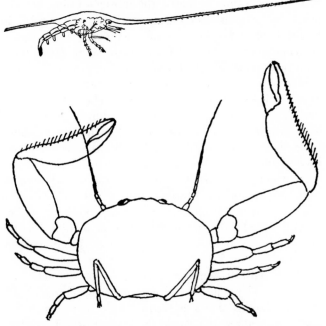

FIG. 12. Porcellanid crab (*Polyonyx macrocheles*). Upper, last zoeal larval stage (x 5½). Lower, full-grown adult (x 3). After Faxon.

Perhaps nothing would break down our sense of the strangeness of crustaceans so much as to discover that their impressions of the external world were received through organs of sense comparable to our own. To ask, then, whether the Crustacea see, hear, feel, smell, and taste as do vertebrate animals, is a fair question and bespeaks a fairer answer than it is, perhaps, possible to give. Naturally, more research on this question has been done on larger and more highly developed Decapoda such as the lobster than on lower Crustacea.

Of actual organs of special sense the lobster seems to have only two kinds: a pair of eyes, and sensory hairs or setae distributed over the entire body and appendages. Though the eyes are rendered prominent by their size and their position on stalks, the lobster's vision may be not very keen as vision goes, and not very useful in bright light. Like the eyes of insects, those of lobsters are compound, with perhaps as many as fourteen thousand facets each of which flashes an impulse to the optic nerve, so that whatever image is registered there is a mosaic of fourteen thousand units. The lobster is by preference a night prowler and in addition confines its activities during the greater part of its life to the dimly lit sea bottom. It is quite possible that the lobster places less reliance on its organs of sight than on the sensory hairs which are by all odds the most useful and versatile sense organs for the lobster's need to "see." However, it appears that in the lobster's case image building may be much less helpful than the detection of motion. For the latter purpose compound eyes are believed to be specially adapted.

These sensory hairs, or setae, are not the relatively insensitive filaments that grow out of the human head: they are hollow shafts of chitin; inside them run nerves which transmit sensations to the central nervous system. Thus we see that the principle of the crustacean organism insofar as it is adapted to sense perception is exactly the same as that of our own organs of taste, touch, and smell.

The function of smelling—which in Crustacea is difficult to distinguish from that of tasting—is performed by the so-called olfactory setae, which are found chiefly on the first antennae and the mouth parts. They are the hairs sensitive to chemical stimuli. As the currents waft fine particles of the lobsterman's bait to the lobster in his hole or on prowl, these olfactory setae catch the scent and lead the victim to follow the trail to the trap.

The sense of touch functions by means of the tactile setae which are scattered over the rest of the lobster's body. From fifty thousand to a hundred thousand are found on the big claws and slender legs alone. Whipping the water with its antennules, trying every crevice with its antennae and big claws, the lobster smells and feels rather than sees its way. Sensitivity to touch is keener in the hairs of certain regions of the lobster's body—such as the tips of the antennules—than in those of other regions, just as in man this sensitivity is keener in the fingertips than in other parts of his body.

The lobster probably does not hear in the sense that mammals do, and it has no organ comparable to the ear of higher vertebrates. But its setae do respond to vibrations in the water just as our ear drum responds to vibrations in the air. The lobster has, however, a pair of organs which were formerly regarded as true ear-sacs, but which are now recognized to be organs of equilibration. These organs enable it to swim in an upright position. They occur as cavities in the basal segments of the first pair of antennae and are furnished with several hundred minute hairs, each richly supplied with nerves. A tiny opening gives access to each cavity and permits the entrance of microscopic grains of sand, many of which become glued to the tips of the hairs and then serve as weights to inform the lobster of the direction of the force of gravity. The whole subject of hearing in

Crustacea is rendered especially absorbing because of the presence in many species of what appears to correspond to a voice. We will devote some time to this subject later (Chapter V).

To conclude our introduction to the lobster's physiology and psychology we need only say that it is excessively pugnacious; that it is a willing cannibal and will as readily eat its own progeny as its own brother if strength will permit; that it shows enough intelligence upon occasion to stalk prey; and that it has been known to store up food, as a dog will hide a bone, for future need. We may now, I hope, go on to meet the lobster's relatives as if they were the family of an old friend.

II. The Family Album

Part I
The Class Crustacea

Every trade and profession has its special vocabulary, and carcinology is no exception. Unfortunately we cannot discuss the vast society of little-known crustaceans without using their names, or at least the names of the larger groups into which they are divided. Earlier carcinologists split the class into two subclasses, Malacostraca and Entomostraca. The latter included such a pageant of diversity that it has had to be replaced by seven subclasses. These are examined in this chapter which forms Part I of "The Family Album." The Malacostraca, eighth of the now generally recognized subclasses into which all Crustacea are organized, are discussed in Chapter III. The eight subclasses are ranked in ascending order, from the more primitive to the more complex and more highly developed forms in the scheme of classification used in this volume and set forth on page 40.

The Decapoda, whose guidance we have been following into the physical and psychological mysteries of the Crustacea, belong to the subclass Malacostraca, the great majority of which have had the grace to keep the number of body segments or true somites at nineteen, a character which makes for ready identification of the membership. The other subclasses have a number of body segments greater or less than nineteen—never nineteen. This diversity of segmentation is a symbol of the diversity to be found in all their structural characteristics.

Classification of the Class Crustacea

(Scheme followed in this account)

Subclass	Number Species	Super-Order	Order
1. Cephalocarida	3 to date		
2. Branchiopoda	800 at least		Anostraca Notostraca Conchostraca Cladocera
3. Ostracoda	2,000 or more		Myodocopa Cladocopa Podocopa Platycopa
4. Mystacocarida	so far only 4		
5. Copepoda	perhaps 5,000		Calanoida Harpacticoida Cyclopoida Notodelphoida Monstrilloida Caligoida Lernaepodoida
6. Branchiura	at least 75		Arguloida
7. Cirripedia	800 to 900		Thoracia Acrothoracia Ascothoracia Apoda Rhizocephala
8. Malacostraca	over 18,000	Leptostraca Hoplocarida Syncarida Pancarida Peracarida Eucarida	Nebaliacea Stomatopoda Anaspidacea Bathynellacea Thermosbaenacea Spelaeogriphacea Mysidacea Cumacea Tanaidacea Isopoda Amphipoda Euphausiacea

Subclass Cephalocarida

Species in this subclass have five coalesced cephalic somites, including two pairs of sensory and three pairs of oral appendages, and nineteen trunk segments of which the first eight carry dwarfed legs of a kind. This subclass is the most recently proposed and was added because the species could not be unequivocally aligned with any other crustaceans. Only three species are known. The largest individual of the first discovered, *Hutchinsoniella macracantha* (Fig. 13), is less than fifteen one-hundredths of an inch in length; the smallest adult is scarcely more than half as long (0.08 inches).

FIG. 13. *Hutchinsoniella macracantha* (x 17). From a model on exhibit in the U.S. National Museum. Courtesy of the Smithsonian Institution.

Cephalocaridans are blind, colorless and grub-like animals living obscurely in silt, mud, or muddy-sand bottoms from a foot below low tide level to a depth of forty or more feet. Their principal nourishment is derived from the organic content of the silt or mud, but with this diet are ingested also microscopic algae and detritus. The place of residence accounts in part for the fact that the first species was not encountered until 1943, and then only while washing soft mud through a very fine meshed screen in the course of a study of the animal and plant life of Long Island Sound mud-bottom communities. In San Francisco Bay a similar investigation yielded a second species, *Lightiella serendipita*, in 1957. Most recently, during a search for copepods known to inhabit the water-filled recesses of shrimp burrows common in intertidal turtle grass flats in Barbados, the third species—and second *Lightiella*, *Lightiella incisa*—was turned up. This species occurs in like surroundings in Puerto Rico, and in intertidal silts as well. Recently, the discoverer of *Hutchinsoniella* has reported taking four specimens of a possible varietal form of this species from off Woods Hole, Massachusetts, at a depth of one hundred sixty four fathoms.

Subclass Branchiopoda

The Branchiopoda, second of the subclasses to claim our attention, breathe—so to speak—through their feet. These feet are usually foliaceous, or leaflike, divided into a number of lobes, each with a gill plate on the outer side which serves as a respiratory organ. This peculiarity of "foot breathing" is almost the only characteristic common to the four orders of Branchiopoda, though the trunk segments are generally distinct and the trunk limbs alike.

Three of the orders, Anostraca (shell-less, fairy shrimp), Notostraca (shell-backed, tadpole shrimp), and Conchostraca (mollusk-shelled, clam shrimp) are, with the exception of a few fairy shrimp, all strictly fresh-water forms. Nearly all, if not all, of their members—living in evanescent bodies of water—are endowed in the egg stage with a remarkable drought-resisting faculty. It is probable that with rare exceptions eggs not subjected to some sort of drying fail to hatch—a most providential arrangement, for if it were possible for eggs to hatch without undergoing the apparent vicissitude of a drought, such eggs as remained when the pool became dry—and when the adults, in consequence, died off—might not have the resistance to endure until the next rainy season. Thus the species would be wiped out with the first complete evaporation of its particular little puddle cosmos.

Usually two kinds of eggs are produced: the so-called summer eggs, purely vegetative and asexual, produced in large numbers and frequently throughout the favorable seasons or periods; and the more resistant dry-season or winter eggs (as the case may be), fewer in number but of greater vitality, and—as a rule, but not always—sexually produced by cross fertilization. In *Limnadia*, among the Conchostraca, no males have ever been discovered. Even in the notostracan *Apus* (which under the nomenclatural law of priority of names of animals, here and henceforth must be known as *Triops*) the males are often of such rare occurrence that their discovery is worthy of note.

The typical anostracan, so-called because of its lack of a carapace, is the fairy shrimp of temperate climes. Many are transparent; such colors as some of them exhibit are largely the result of refraction—evanescent, iridescent greens and blues, which appear at times on some of the appendages over a ground of translucent creamy white with reddish trimming. Though common in many parts of the world, fairy shrimps are seldom seen except when especially sought after. Their occurrence, too, seems largely subject to all the vagaries of *Triops.*

The *Triops* (Fig. 14), which belongs to the order Notostraca, a name that refers to the shell-like carapace of its members, looks remarkably like a small horseshoe crab. It may measure nearly three inches in length, and it was long considered the largest of all branchiopods. Recently, however, *Lepidurus lynchi,* differing generically in the possession of a small posterior plate attached to the telson, was found to grow up to an inch longer. Top billing, however, goes to the fairy shrimp *Branchinecta gigas,* found in eastern Oregon, which measures up to five and a quarter inches. The chief claim of *Triops* to popular attention is its inconstancy of habit. Though not uncommon from year to year on the continent of Europe it makes some very curious skips and jumps in its seasonal appearance, and one cannot definitely count on finding it in the same locality two years in succession. Frequently it fails to appear in a given area for a number of years. In England, well populated with amateur and professional naturalists, *Triops* was first recorded in 1738 as a "sort of insect," from Bex[le]y Common. It was next seen in 1816 in a temporary pool in Hampshire. About 1837 it appeared in Bristol, and in 1907 it was reported over the border in Scotland. The next recorded appearance under *natural conditions* in the Hampshire pool was in 1948, a lapse of 132 years.

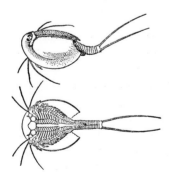

FIG. 14. *Triops longicaudatus,* from Wyoming. Dorsal and ventral views. After Sars.

Though it had not been observed living in that pool in all that time, interested investigators had twice hatched *Triops* from dried mud obtained there—in 1934 and 1937. *Triops*, like other branchiopods, produces eggs that hatch the same season, and it perpetuates the species by means of drought and winter-resistant eggs which must be exposed to a period of dessication before they will develop. Why they fail to appear in the same pool except at long intervals remains a great mystery. The fact that England is a well-watered country with few pools that dry up each year may well account for its sporadic appearance there.

Artemia, the brine shrimp, is perhaps the most widely distributed branchiopod in the world. It occurs almost everywhere in strongly saline bodies of water of any appreciable size and in pools or pans where sea water is evaporated with the sun's aid. *Artemia* is a very plastic form responding readily, in external appearance at least, to changes in environmental conditions, especially to the salinity and alkalinity of the body of water in which it finds itself. Many different forms have been described, all variants of one species, except perhaps our North American representative of the genus. From Great Salt Lake, the late A. E. Verrill of Yale University described *Artemia gracilis* (Fig. 15), a species believed to be in good standing.

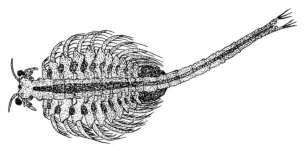

FIG. 15. *Artemia gracilis,* from Great Salt Lake. After Jensen.

In some of our western saline bodies of water, *Artemia* seasonally occurs in such prodigious numbers as to color red or brownish-red the water in which they live. They eat small green algae which in the process of digestion appear to turn red, usually giving the animal a conspicuous coloration. In Great Salt Lake their numbers at times are beyond comprehension, forming great windrows stretching across the lake as far as the eye can see.

They are also abundant in the salt works in south San Francisco, and it was there that Alvin Seale, first curator of the Steinhart Aquarium of the California Academy of Sciences, thought of feeding them to his charges. They proved to be just the right food for aquarium fishes, easy to come by and available in endless quantity. Today the brine-shrimp business has arrived. Frozen, they are stocked in pet stores, and eggs—drought and freeze resistant—are sold to fish fanciers. In the San Francisco Bay area alone, the industry is valued at $350,000. To get at the dollar value of the industry across the nation, we must add $50,000 for Great Salt Lake, $30,000 for Mono Lake, California, and $25,000 for San Diego.

The third branchiopod order, the Conchostraca (Fig. 16), gets its name from the development of the carapace

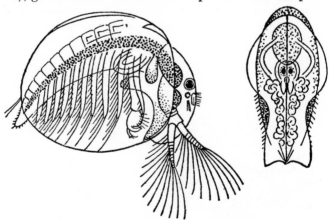

FIG. 16. Branchiopod (*Limnetis*) with a bivalve carapace. Lateral view of female and frontal view of male (x 9). After Sars.

of its members into a bivalve shell, completely inclosing the body and limbs and closely resembling the shell of a small mollusk. A similar development has taken place in most of the Cladocera, the fourth order, although in these crustaceans the head is left free.

The Cladocera are named "water-fleas," from their jumping mode of progression. They have none of the erratic characteristics of *Triops*, and though of very small size, even microscopic, they occur in such great numbers that they furnish the basic food supply of most of the commercial fishes of the Great Lakes. These lakes are great nurseries for fish and Crustacea. Cladocera and copepods are the primary, if not the exclusive, food of the young of many of these indigenous fish, and indirectly of the young of piscivorous species as the yellow pike or walleye, since these prey to a great extent upon crustacean feeders such as smelt and alewives. Some species of Cladocera are marine and form such considerable swarms at sea that they surely contribute to the food of salt-water fishes.

Daphnia pulex, one of the best-known cladocerans, bears in its specific name the brand of its somewhat superficial resemblance to the flea. This diminutive crustacean hides much delicate beauty from our gross vision. Under the microscope there is much to be learned about the reproductive habits of the branchiopods. Something has been said of the two sorts of eggs laid by members of the preceding orders. *Daphnia,* in common with the other cladocerans, carries the eggs around in a brood pouch inclosed by the dorsal part of the valves of her carapace (Fig. 17). This serves as a nursery in which the eggs develop and where the young hatch out in a form not unlike the parent and are sheltered till fairly well grown. Thus it is that we find no free-swimming larval forms among the Cladocera. The off-spring are nourished in quite a remarkable manner. For the long period of their sheltered existence, the egg yolk with which they hatched into the world would not alone

FIG. 17. Representative cladocerans. Left, female *Daphnia pulex* (x 5). Center, *Leptodora kindtii* (x 1½). Right, female *Scaphole-beris mucronata* (x 18), using surface film of water as a support. After Keilhack, Pearse, and Scourfield.

suffice, so as they grow they feed also upon a secretion from the walls of the brood chamber.

This is the course of the parthenogenetic young, which consist usually of several successive generations of females. But sooner or later, with the approach of winter or the drying up of the body of water in which they live, true sexual males and females hatch out. These in turn unite to produce fewer (usually one or two) but larger eggs, heavy with much yolk and with a thick, resistant shell. Like the other eggs, these pass into the brood-chamber, which now becomes modified and thickened. In *Daphnia*, this transformation becomes quite marked; the valves of the carapace take on a peculiar shape like a saddle; and so the carapace in this genus bears the technical name of ephippium derived through the Latin from two Greek words meaning "on a horse." The purpose of this modification is revealed in the next molt, when the ephippium becomes detached from the rest of the shell and closes snugly about the eggs it is to guard, thus protecting them until the next favorable season.

These winter eggs, like those of other lower Crustacea, are very drought resistant. Mud taken from the dried-up Pool of Gihon, at Jerusalem—a pool whose history goes back some twenty-five hundred years—was moistened, and there hatched out not less than seven species of Crustacea, of which at least two were new to science at the time. One bit of mud from this pool was alternately moistened and dried out in the laboratory year after year for twenty-four years, thus simulating the wet and dry seasons of its normal environment; and each year until an accident terminated the experiment, another generation of Crustacea hatched out. Even after other portions of this dry mud were laid away for nine and ten years, Crustacea hatched out when they were moistened.

Of the Cladocera, only a few are not "shelled." The carapace of shell-less forms is transformed into a distinct and conspicuous "sac" which functions as the brood pouch. These aberrant members of the order present such radical departures from the usual cladoceran form that they constitute a group apart, in which is included *Leptodora kindtii* (Fig. 17), without doubt the largest cladoceran, the female reaching a length of nearly three-quarters of an inch. Any other species, when full grown, is of good size if it measures as much as a sixteenth of an inch from head to tail.

Some cladocerans have adjusted themselves to a life in the mud, and the shells of these are often overgrown with algae. But adaptations of an extraordinary nature have been developed by the species that lead a swimming existence to enable them to minimize the energy expended in keeping afloat. A few, including *Scapholeberis* (Fig. 17), hold themselves to the surface of the water by making fast to the surface film. For this purpose they possess specially modified, water-repellant scales and setae on their ventral surfaces. Swimming in their normal position, back downwards, they pierce the surface film and hang thus, drifting about, foraging along the surface of the water at will or releasing their hold to dive readily to the bottom. Swimming ventral side up seems to be the normal method in many, if not most, of the cladoceran crustaceans.

Advantageous as the surface film is to *Scapholeberis,*
it is deadly to numerous other less well adapted Crustacea, including *Daphnia.* If one of this genus happens to
break through the surface film, it is almost as serious in
its consequences as for a man to fall out of a third-story
window; for upon penetrating the film it tends to fall
over on its side, perfectly helpless in the powerful and
relentless grip of the surface tension of the water. This
is the same force that enables a steel needle to float in a
glass of water. The only escape for *Daphnia* from such a
hopeless condition lies in the release that a violent
disturbance of the water might afford, unless the animal
happens to be about to molt. In such a happy chance,
like the thief that escapes by leaving his coat in his
pursuer's hands, the *Daphnia* is able to slip out of the
old shell or chitinous housing, which remains floating at
the surface of the water, while, newly molted, it regains
the safe, cool depths. Helpless individuals of this genus
have been observed at times in such numbers that they
formed a scum upon the surface of the water, many
square yards in area.

Subclass Ostracoda

Abundant in all seas and lakes and in almost all
bodies of water, down to the merest roadside puddle, the
Ostracoda (Fig. 18) probably stand next to the Copepoda
among Crustacea in their importance to zoological economy. They often occur in such teeming numbers as to
lend color to the water. Some of them exist at great
altitudes, one species—*Cypris altissima*—having been
found in a pool fed by melting snow twelve thousand
feet above sea level. Another species, *Gigantocypris,* has
been taken from the depths of the ocean six hundred
fathoms down. Appropriately named, this species is
nearly an inch in length and a giant indeed compared to
the really small forms measuring a hundredth of an
inch. There is also a "terrestrial" ostracod which lives in

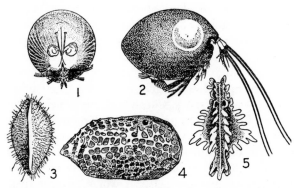

FIG. 18. Representative ostracods. 1, frontal view of a female *Gigantocypris*, largest of the ostracods (x 1); 2-5, other species (much enlarged). After Müller.

damp humus in the Knysna Forest, South Africa. As would be expected, the locomotory appendages of this species, *Mesocypris terrestris,* are more powerfully developed than those of other members of the genus.

Among Crustacea the Ostracoda are remarkable for the small number of their appendages and their unsegmented or, at best, very indistinctly segmented body, inclosed in a bivalve shell fashioned from the carapace. Few other crustaceans are so completely encompassed by their housings. So much do they resemble small mollusks that frequently at the National Museum we are asked to identify the tiny "shells" this or that correspondent has unexpectedly found in some body of water.

But few as the ostracod's appendages may be, they are very powerfully developed and fulfill all the essential functions performed by the more generous number with which other crustaceans are endowed. Ostracods depend on the first and second pairs of antennae for a variety of services. In some forms these are the only appendages that protrude from the shell. Aside from their sensory function, they are the locomotive organs, and most efficient ones at that, whether the mode of progression be swimming, creeping, or burrowing.

Of the food and feeding of ostracods there is still much to be learned. The more closely observed freshwater forms seem to be omnivorous, subsisting upon almost anything that comes to hand, living or dead, animal or vegetable. Marine forms, though more difficult to observe, seem to feed largely on diatoms and other plants of the sea and shore. Carnivorous tendencies crop up in some; all in all, by mere press of numbers, they must play an enormously important role as scavengers and as intermediates in the conversion of food material into a shape utilizable by larger animals. Certain species suck the juices of marine plants, for which purpose their upper and lower lips are organized, with the jaws, into a peculiar sucking tube. Incidentally, the ostracods that parasitize other animals have a similar adaptation. Only a few such parasitic ostracods are known, one having been taken from a fish, a second from a sea-lily, and two others from different crustaceans.

Some marine ostracods have been found with the remains of copepods in their alimentary tract. These species ensnare their prey by means of a sticky secretion spread over the fore part of the shell. Here any copepod that comes in contact with it is held fast, much as flypaper holds a fly. The glands of ostracods and their secretions are quite a study in themselves. Certain genera—*Pyrocypris* and *Cypridina*—are even luminous, thanks to a phosphorescent secretion which they can expel in clouds and so possibly foil a pursuing enemy. In others the fluid expressed from the glands serves to agglutinate the sand in which the ostracods burrow, and so provide their builders with definite tubular retreats. Others have a spinning gland, from which issues a sticky substance that quickly hardens and forms a thread. With this the ostracod, after the manner of familiar spiders, weaves a network to secure itself to the immediate surroundings or to enable it to climb about where foothold otherwise would be precarious.

In common with a number of other Crustacea, many ostracods reproduce parthenogenetically; that is, the females bear eggs which are capable of hatching and producing the succeeding generation of ostracods without the intervention of a male. Under experimental conditions in an aquarium, successive generations of females have been kept going for as long as thirty years. As in the case of some Conchostraca, males of some ostracod species have never been found. Like our branchiopod water-flea, ostracod mothers may carry the eggs and sometimes even the young. Often the eggs are deposited on seaweeds, or merely shed into the water.

In vitality, also, the eggs of ostracods share honors with those of some other fresh-water crustaceans, remaining viable in dried mud for years. G. O. Sars, of Norway, one of the foremost carcinologists of all time, made a practice of soliciting bits of puddle, pond, and ditch bottom from all parts of the world. He was thus able to hatch and describe no end of new and unusual species of ostracods without the expense entailed by special expeditions in search of them. Ostracods are unique in that even some of the adult forms, in spite of extreme desiccation, may be brought back to a condition approaching normal by soaking them in water, though they may never actually come to life, as do the eggs on hatching.

Subclass Mystacocarida

There is a bit of a story here of how one investigation leads to others, and in this case led to the discovery of a type of crustacean on which this subclass is based.

Intrigued by the receipt of some unusual copepods which the late nematologist N. A. Cobb discovered amid the grains of sand of intertidal beaches about Woods Hole, Massachusetts, the biologist Charles B. Wilson made further studies of this area and was able to describe a number of new species of copepods. The uniqueness of the habitat and of copepods adapted to life within it alerted Donald Zinn and Robert Pennak to undertake an ecologic study of such beaches. Among the copepods washed from those sands were some minute, colorless fellows, not more than a fiftieth of an inch long. Seeking an identification, these two men consulted Dr. Wilson, whose response was "Not a copepod." This was a challenge. Zinn and Pennak set to work dissecting those tiny creatures to learn what manner of beast they had. General body plan, structure of the antennae, and more remotely, the mouth parts, pointed to a fairly close relationship to the Copepoda. Bodily organization and appendages pointed also toward the tanaids and isopods. Stranger yet, the internal organization in some ways suggested distant branchiopod affinities, and the almost over-developed cephalic appendages and reduced thoracic limbs gave quite a larval appearance.

With the publication of Pennak and Zinn's findings in 1943 and their proposal of the Mystacocarida as a new order of Crustacea (this was later raised to a subclass), a hunt was on around the world for mystacocarideans. In the twenty years intervening since the original description of *Derocheilocaris typicus,* only two other species have been found. One, *Derocheilocaris remani,* occurs in several places along the Spanish, French, and Italian Riviera, where it lives, as does *Derocheilocaris typicus* (Fig. 19) in New England, interstitially, several inches below the surface of intertidal sand beaches. The other species hails from an island off the coast of southern Chile, where it was dredged from a coarse sand bottom in thirteen or fourteen fathoms—a depth far in excess of any at which the other two species were found. It has been assumed that *Derocheilocaris galvarini* is a strictly salt-water species. But in the depths where it is found there may be upwelling fresh water— just as there is an admixture of fresh ground water with the salt water of the sea in the case of the Mediterranean beaches where *D. remani* was found, and quite possibly also in the New England localities.

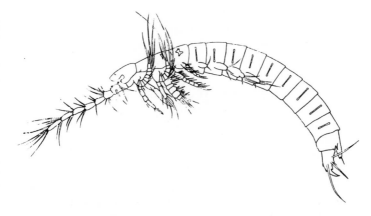

FIG. 19. *Derocheilocaris typicus.* Lateral view of female (about
x 195). From Pennak.

Subclass Copepoda

Some of the mighty whalebone whales—among the
world's largest mammals—and fish so small as to be
microscopic are alike beholden for their existence to
copepods, the "oar-footed" crustaceans. More fish and
other aquatic creatures feed on these tiny crustaceans
than on any other one kind of animal known. The free
swimming copepods, in the main, form the base of the
pyramid of marine life, transforming, as do the ostracods, the microscopic vegetable life of the sea and
inland waters into food which can be utilized by animals larger than themselves. In the sea the copepods
have no rival as food for fishes, and even in the Great
Lakes they run the cladocerans a close second. The
whitefish, in its heyday one of the most important fresh-
water food fishes in North America, feeds almost wholly
on copepods and cladocerans. The copepods are therefore of more than mere academic significance to man.
Like the cladocerans and ostracods, the copepods com-
pensate for their microscopic size by their unbelievably
large numbers. They multiply more rapidly than the
proverbial flies. A rough estimate of the number of individuals produced annually in a mere ten cubic meters
of Baltic sea water is nine billion (Fig. 20).

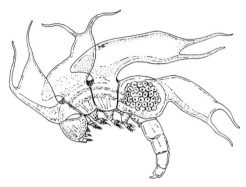

FIG. 20. Female butterfly copepod (*Notopterophorus papilio*) with eggs (x 15). After Sars.

Not all copepods are the helpless victims of the appetites of other organisms. The race has predatory capacities of its own and, moreover, has made parasitism a fine art. It has displayed a genius for adapting itself to live at the expense of practically every other living thing in the sea. Any scheme of classifying copepods divides them quite naturally into free swimming and parasitic forms.

Many free swimming copepods are active forms, others are more or less passive floaters, while still others are jumpers and skippers. Some of the latter are so energetic and occur in such immense numbers that they give the most startling illusion of rain at sea, although there may not be a cloud in sight above the horizon. In particular I have reference to *Anomalocera pattersoni*, a form that lives close to the surface of the sea and for which "flying fish of the copepod world" would not be an inappropriate designation. The Norwegian fishermen call them "Bla-ate" (blue bait) and hail a "shower" of them as a good sign of the approach of the summer herrings, which feed upon them in vast numbers. Among the floating Copepoda are some of the most notable members of this subclass, long to be remembered for their splendor of form.

Pelagic copepods may first attract our attention, but they have hundreds of bottom-dwelling relatives. Even the hard-packed sandy beaches of our shores support a considerable copepod population. In a single pail of sandy water taken from a New England shore, Professor Wilson gathered eight hundred specimens belonging to twenty-five species of Copepoda. Marine copepods have also been found in the abysses of the ocean—three miles and more below the surface.

Much has been made of the viability of the eggs of ostracods, but the tenacity with which some tide-pool copepods cling to life is equally amazing. Along rocky coasts one finds life in spray-fed pools above high water mark. These often run low on water and sometimes evaporate down to caked salt. Dr. J. H. Fraser of the Plymouth, England, Marine Biological Laboratory became interested in the durability of the copepod *Tigriopus fulvus*. He dipped a half jar full of water from one of these pools and this was sealed tightly and set aside. In the course of the first seven weeks the activity of the contained animal life declined considerably; after eighteen months all animal and plant life was apparently dead or dormant. After twenty-four months the jar was opened and placed by an open window; the contents were stirred but nothing was added. Within a month a covering of blue-green developed and green algae appeared. Two species of copepods, including the *Tigriopus*, and a few ostracods became active. As the copepods were stunted in size, it was concluded that they had not developed from resting eggs but rather had been slightly active during the time the jar was sealed. The strength of the "will" to survive the most adverse conditions is indicated by such reflowering when conditions again become favorable.

Of the widespread fresh-water copepods the best-known genus is *Cyclops*, so named because, like all typical copepods, it had but a single median eye in the middle of its forehead. The running water of streams seems to be more scantily populated with copepods than that of pools or lakes. Fresh-water copepods share the common name of water-fleas with the cladocerans and the ostracods; also they share with these forms their varied and unusual habitats the world over. The fresh-water copepods are perennial, like weeds in the field. Some species are strictly summer forms, and others seem to thrive best in the colder parts of the year. Some cold-water copepods, like *Cyclops bicuspidatus,* are said to spend the summer months in cocoons formed of mud and other bottom materials held together by a glutinous secretion.

Turning to the amazing story of the parasitic copepods, we learn—as the result of Professor Wilson's extensive studies of them—that in no other group of Crustacea has parasitism led to such diversity of structure and life history. The parasitic habit of life has been adopted to a greater or less degree by many different families in the group, and every step in the transition from the more normal free-swimming type to a completely parasitic one is represented. There is scarcely a group of animals that is not adversely affected by one copepod or another. The modifications of structure which parasitism has effected in some species of Copepoda are so great that no one could be expected to guess their crustacean relationship. But by their larvae you shall know them; for no matter what their later life may be, most of them leave the egg as a minute nauplius (Fig. 21). Normally following the nauplius and metanauplius forms (of which there may be several stages) the larva transforms into the copepodid stage, which is a precursor of the final adult stage. Some of the parasitic forms pass through the nauplius stages while still within the egg and hatch as a free-swimming copepodid. At this stage, the tiny animal seeks a host to which to attach itself, subsequently undergoing transformation into a rather strange adult— usually little more than a feeding, reproductive mechanism for producing further parasitic copepods.

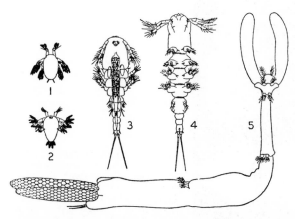

FIG. 21. Stages in the development of the parasitic copepod, *Lernaea variabilis.* 1, nauplius (x 28); 2, metanauplius (x 28); 3, female fourth copepodid larva (x 24); 4, male fourth copepodid larva (x 28); 5, adult female (x 8). After Wilson.

The rather thoroughly investigated *Lernaea,* of not uncommon occurrence on certain tropical and temperate fresh-water fishes, will illustrate the life history of the group (Fig. 22). The free swimming copepodid larvae attach themselves to the gills of a convenient fish host of the right species, and there male and female mate while still in a larval stage. Thereupon the male, his usefulness at an end, apparently dies, like the drone of the beehive. The female, on the other hand, deserts her first fish host to settle down on a second host, this time on the outside of its body instead of on the gills. Once established she becomes transformed into the adult, as we know her, of the species she represents, and becomes a permanent, fixed parasite for the rest of her natural life. For purposes of secure attachment, the sides of the cephalothorax grow out laterally as "horns," which may extend into the flesh of the host or else become firmly affixed to its scales; in either case, however, the head burrows in the tissues of the host in search of nourishment. This treatment often causes a good-sized lump or tumorous

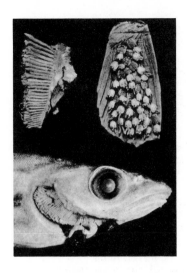

FIG. 22. Parasitic copepods on fishes. Upper left, *Lernaeopoda* on gill of salmon. Upper right, thirty-two individuals of *Lepeophtheirus* on fin of flounder. Lower, *Lernaeocera* on gill of whiting. After Scott. Courtesy of the Ray Society, London.

growth to develop on the host, and this may be raw and bleeding within. It has a perforation through which the hinder part of the parasite projects in order that her young shall have no difficulty in taking up a free-swimming existence when once the fertilized eggs begin to hatch. Although *Lernaea* is a pronounced parasite, the free-swimming larvae of the genus are exceedingly active and very tenacious of life.

A list of the hosts of the copepods in a given body of water is well nigh a catalogue of its fish population. The poor fishes are attacked in every conceivable manner and in almost every conceivable part of their anatomy.

The spiracle of the gray skate harbors *Charopinus,* a fellow a full two inches long. The nostrils of the cod are the chosen home of another copepod, which evidently feeds on the mucus secreted there. As many as twenty-nine individuals have been taken from the nostrils of one cod. To still other genera the eyes of their hosts offer the one worthwhile abode, and they become so embedded in these organs that only the most painstaking dissection can remove them entirely. One of these—*Phrixocephalus diversus* Wilson—burrows completely through the fish's eyeball, halting only when its head again emerges on the side opposite to that on which it entered; there it invests the outer wall of the retina with its mouth so as to draw on the rich blood supply of the network of vessels nourishing the retina. Of course, the sight in the organ attacked is forever doomed. Other species of copepods burrow into the body cavity of the host and attack the heart, liver, and other vital organs.

The largest and the most striking of the copepods, genus *Pennella*, are found as parasites on at least eight genera of fish, including the giant swordfish, the shark sucker, the gigantic ocean sunfish, and the flying fish. As can be seen in Figure 23, the abdomen of *Pennella* carries a series of branched featherlike processes arranged in a row on either side. These so resemble feathers in appearance that not only do they give the genus its name, for *Pennella* is the diminutive of the Latin *penna,* "feather," but the species infesting flying fish are popularly known as the "feathers" of this soaring inhabitant of the tropic seas.

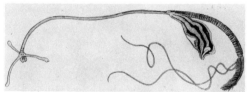

FIG. 23. Parasitic copepod (*Pennella balaenopterae*) from a finner whale and itself carrying the barnacle *Conchoderma*. After Turner.

Pennella, as well as some other parasitic copepods, victimizes other animals besides fish. *Pennella balaenopterae* is found in considerable numbers on the common rorqual or finner whale—one of the largest of mammals. This species may attain a length of twelve and a half inches not including the ovisacs or egg strings, which sometimes trail out behind the body of the parasite for a distance as great again. The possession of egg strings or egg sacs, incidentally, is very often a distinctive copepod character, whether the form be marine or fresh-water, free-swimming or parasitic.

On the whale too, is found another copepod, *Balaenophilus unisetus*, a very tiny fellow compared to *Pennella*. The adult female is less than an eighth of an inch long; the smaller male is but two thirds as large. The species was first discovered by Carl Aurivillius in 1879, on a sulphur-bottom whale that had been hauled into a whaling station in northern Norway. The copepods were present in such incredible numbers that they formed conspicuous yellowish-white patches on the baleen plates of their host. In the next eighty-five years mention of this seldom noticed species did not appear in literature more than eight times; most were additional records for the northern hemisphere, but it also was discovered in the southern half of the world, on baleen whales frequenting the seas about Antarctica.

Throughout their lives these copepods cling tenaciously to the baleen by means of the powerful clasping organs into which their maxillipeds and first legs have developed. Without these organs they could not maintain a foothold in the rush of water that pours over and between the fringes of the baleen plates of the hosts when feeding.

The observations made by Drs. Vervoort of Leiden, Netherlands, and Tranter of Cronulla, N.S.W. in Australia (1961), led them to remark that this interesting copepod was more of a commensal, "a feeder at the same table" than a parasite. In truth, this copepod seems a "hitchhiker," feeding upon minute green algae growing profusely on the host's baleen plates. There seems little doubt that these algae are the principal if not the sole food of the copepods. Their oral appendages are perfectly adapted for scraping and not for filter feeding; and the contents of the stomachs examined consist of whole and partially digested unicellular algae filled with green plastids.

One may wonder how these tiny and firmly attached copepods or their young get from one host to another as whales on the move often do twelve miles an hour and have been clocked at twenty during a chase. To and from their breeding grounds they travel relatively close together in schools, but it is more likely that the transfer takes place during the breeding season in tropic waters, when the whales are more closely bunched together than when migrating or feeding on the high seas.

It would seem that animals that spend but a part of their lives in water are as helpless as deep-sea dwellers in escaping these widely distributed and marvelously adapted copepod pests. In Japan the genus *Lernaea* has even been found on an amphibian, the Japanese salamander. However, this is the only vertebrate other than fish and marine mammals known to be infested with parasitic copepods.

There is no conception of *noblesse oblige* among the Copepoda and they willingly levy tribute on any and all convenient crustacean relatives. Even the land crab of the West Indies, the big bluish-gray *Cardisoma guanhumi*, which but once a year goes down to the sea to hatch its young, supports two known species of parasitic copepods on its gills; and as many as thirty copepods have been obtained from the gills of a single crab host. These parasites, of necessity, must have their lives so beautifully attuned to that of the host that they, too, can take advantage of the crab's annual dip in the ocean to perpetuate their own kind, which in turn will infest other land crabs as they are spawning. Since this dip endures but ten days at the most, the adjustment is a most remarkable provision of nature. There can be no doubt that it exists, however; for though the crab's gills, while that animal is on the land, are moist enough to keep the copepods alive, it does not appear to be moist enough to permit adequate aeration of the eggs.

Copepods of the family Choniostomatidae are found

parasitic on other crustaceans exclusively. One might call them microscopic nits. They bore a little hole in the shell of the host to obtain sustenance; and the female, at least, spends the balance of her life in complete dependence. Shrimps of several kinds, mysids, and especially amphipods, isopods, and cumaceans all are attacked by these tiny beggars.

The starfishes and their kind, collectively known as echinoderms, likewise contribute to the support of parasitic copepods. Four species of these crustaceans have been taken from three different kinds of ophiurans, as the brittle stars are technically termed. The parasites often establish themselves within the host and usually produce noticeable malformations or galls.

Parasitic copepods also prey on hard-shelled mollusks. While still in the nauplius stage they find their way into the gill tubes of the sand clam *Mya*; and they are found in two species of mussels, in the toothsome scallops, in razor clams, in cockle shells, and in some species of oysters. *Pennella* larvae have been found on the gills of the cuttlefish—a mollusk with an internal shell; nor have the nudibranchs—sluglike mollusks without shells— escaped giving food and shelter to uninvited copepod guests.

Degeneration or specialization among parasitic copepods is carried to the extreme in those forms that live on certain marine annelid worms and also in those that live on certain other crustaceans. In the best known of these highly specialized forms the adult female is entirely without appendages and is attached by a tubular process which ramifies within the body of the host. The males are also limbless; and, rather remarkably, they never escape the last larval stage—in this case the first copepodid stage—spending their lives attached, with other males, to a female of their species.

The more one delves into the relations of animals to one another, the more often one finds illustrated Dean Swift's oft misquoted doggerel:

So Nat'ralists observe, a Flea
Hath smaller Fleas that on him prey.
And these have smaller Fleas to bite 'em,
And so proceed *ad infinitum.*

Copepods are no exception. *Pennella,* which parasitizes
the whale, is, in turn, the unwilling transport of a
peculiar barnacle, *Conchoderma virgatum.* The barnacle
in this case is a passive parasite, making use of but not
actually subsisting on its host. It merely adds to the sum
total of the burdens which the copepod is called upon to
carry through its marine existence. Dr. Wilson told of a
Pennella four inches in length to which were attached
eighteen *Conchoderma,* the latter forming a mass many
times the size of the copepod. Attached to the outside of
their host, where they encounter all that floats in the
water, *Pennellas* very quickly become covered with algae, ciliate infusoria, hydroids, and even barnacles, as
noted above. Seaweeds, too, find their place on these
copepod parasites. Though troublesome to the parasite
on account of their weight and bulk, these added organisms are not to be considered superparasites, for they
do not feed on the copepods to which they attach
themselves.

Subclass Branchiura

These parasitic "fish-lice" in the form of the genus
Argulus (Fig. 24) have been met with on frequent occasions in goldfish aquariums. Unlike copepods, argulids

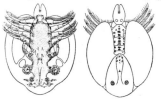

FIG. 24. A parasitic branchiuran (*Argulus trilineata*) sometimes
found on goldfish. Dorsal and ventral views of a female. Note in
the ventral view suckers and hooks on the antennae by which she
attaches herself to the fish (x 5). After Wilson.

possess paired compound eyes. They feed on the blood of their host, and those that infest migratory fish are strongly suspected of being able to change with their host from salt to fresh water or the reverse. Another peculiarity of these crustaceans is that they do not carry their eggs around with them, as do copepods, but deposit them on some favorable surface on the bottom, or, if in aquariums, sometimes on the glass sides. If an argulid does not succeed in finding a host of the species on which it is specifically parasitic, it has been known to live on almost any other fish, and even on tadpoles. The common European *Argulus foliaceus* has been found on some thirty-four species of fish, native and exotic aquarium species, and on the tadpoles of at least five species of amphibians.

Argulids are ready swimmers, but progress rather peculiarly—by somersaulting through the water, as it were. An external parasite needs an efficient means of anchorage. In the argulids, the anterior maxillipeds are modified into powerful muscular sucking disks; and "by a walking motion of these same disks they scuttle about over the fish's skin so long as it remains moist." The suckers lose their adhesive power on a dry surface. Further to keep from slipping backward off the fish as it darts through the water the argulid's antennae are provided with stout hooks, spines, and bristles, which at the slightest backward movement grip fast to the skin of the fish. The greater the speed and the water pressure, the tighter the argulids stick.

Subclass Cirripedia

The subclass Cirripedia gets its name from the cirrus-like or feathery feet of its better-known representatives—the barnacles, order Thoracica, the first of five into which Cirrepedia are classified today.

The Thoracica comprise three suborders—Lepado-morpha, the stalked form, and Balanomorpha and Verru-

FIG. 25. Stalked (*Lepas*) and sessile (*Balanus*) barnacles.

comorpha, both sessile forms but basically different (Fig. 25). The most widely known of the Balanomorpha are the common rock or acorn barnacles.

Barnacles of the suborder Lepadomorpha as a rule are attached to some support from which they never escape. The body, however, with its inclosing valves, is elevated on a stalk, or peduncle, which may be fleshy, leathery, or scaly. The members of the Lepadomorpha may vary quite widely in appearance and habitat. In some the body is heavily armored with calcareous plates, while in others the plates are incompletely calcified or present only as vestiges. Most are fixed immovably in one spot, but some are attached to floating jellyfish of various kinds and are limited in distribution only by the range of their hosts. These barnacles have in their peduncles well-developed cement glands, the secretion of which forms a yellowish, vesicular ball—in some cases as much as an inch and a half in diameter—which serves to keep the barnacle afloat should it fail to contact a jellyfish or some floating object. At sea, a number of these barnacles occasionally cluster together to form a common float.

The sessile Balanomorpha are often called "acorn shells" or "acorn barnacles" because of their supposed resemblance to the acorn; to others they are known as "rock barnacles," as they are omnipresent on rocky shores around the world. It was surely one of these that Thomas Huxley had in mind when he so aptly described a barnacle as an essentially shrimp-like form that has become attached by the head to some submerged surface; that has incased itself in an armor of stout plates, often fused together; and that kicks food into its mouth by means of its filamentous, feathery-appearing feet. The soft body of the animal is surrounded by an immovable shelly wall or palisade of plates which grows attached to some means of support, such as stones, piling, ships' bottoms, bodies of other animals, or seaweed. The calcareous covering or wall of the barnacle serves it, in its more or less helpless condition of fixation, as a protection from all aggressors not strong enough to crush it. The Balanus-type barnacles of the genus *Acasta*, with one exception live embedded in the outer surface of sponges where perhaps they benefit from food materials borne to their vicinity by the water currents generated by the sponge in its feeding. The exceptional *Acasta* embeds in a gorgonian, a species of soft coral.

Much the smallest suborder of the Thoracica in number of species—fifty or so—the sessile Verrucomorpha superficially have the look of underprivileged rock barnacles. They are asymmetrical and possess extraordinarily unequal valves. Despite the small number of species, Verrucomorpha are distributed around the world—in the Atlantic from Iceland to Cape Horn; in the Pacific from Tierra del Fuego, up along the coast to Peru, to Hawaii and to Panay in the Philippines, and in the Red Sea. They are found close to shore and in great depths—some at over seventeen hundred fathoms. One from 913 fathoms was attached to a volcanic pebble.

Representatives of the other orders of Cirripedia seldom meet the eye, being for the most part relatively inconspicuous parasites, plaguing a variety of invertebrate hosts. Excepting the Rhizocephala they contain few species. Of the order Apoda, just one lone specimen is known—a fifth-of-an-inch long *Proteolepas*, found by Charles Darwin within a West Indian stalked barnacle. Its pair of adhering antennules with cement glands are all that associate this little maggot-like orphan with the cirripedes; a second one has yet to be found.

Of the Ascothoracia there may be upwards of sixty species; of the Acrothoracia perhaps only a third as many; but the Rhizocephala number well over two hundred. The species of these three orders are all chitinous-skinned. They neither occupy limestone houses nor are they clothed, even in part, with calcareous plates, or valves. All are parasites of a kind, either boring into their hosts for shelter or feeding upon them.

The Acrothoracia are the boring forms. They spend their adult lives buried in excavations made in shells of other barnacles, in stony corals, the plates of sea urchins, and a variety of snail and clam shells, usually those of living animals. The most interesting perhaps is the exceptional *Trypetesa*, which bores only into dead shells inhabited by hermit crabs. Their cirriform appendages and mouth parts, for feeding in typical barnacle fashion, leave no doubt regarding their true relationship.

But with the organisms aligned with the Ascothoracia, it is the other way around. Their claim of cirripede relationship is not well established. Their means and modes of taking nourishment tend to set them apart. More will have to be known about their life histories before the question of relationship can be fully resolved. A number are external parasites, ectoparasites, with few and much reduced, not in the least cirriform appendages. Their mouth parts are adapted for piercing tissues and sucking the body fluids of their hosts—fleshy or soft corals, gorgonians, various starfish, sea-urchins, sea-stars, and sea-lilies. Others live within the body cavities of their hosts—which also include starfish, sea-urchins, and stony corals. These derive their sustenance from the host's body fluids, by means of absorptive lobes or papillae.

But after all, how is one to know that any of these barnacles or other cirripedes of strange shapes and varied habits are crustaceans? For many, many years barnacles were considered shellfish and mollusks, along with clams, oysters, snails, mussels, and the like. The clue to their crustacean nature lies in their growth stages (Fig. 26), as does that of the parasitic copepods we already have considered. It is scarcely believable that the young barnacle emerges from the egg as a mobile nauplius; but with few exceptions it does. It progresses through a number of stages with little change in form until it reaches a definite metanauplius stage, which lasts but a short time. At the next molt the young barnacle transforms into a cypris-stage, so called because the bivalved shell with which the cirriped is provided in this stage gives it a resemblance to the real *Cypris,* an ostracod. As the larva at this stage possesses the full complement of appendages of the adult barnacle, it is in all essentials a free-swimming cirriped. When the cypris larva finds or lights upon a suitable place of settlement, to this it attaches itself by means of the cement glands with which it is provided, and goes about the business of becoming a recognizable barnacle for the rest of its natural life. The free-swimming larval stages permit the otherwise sessile, sedentary barnacles to scatter to the four corners of the marine world. Some are found only in very restricted localities; while others, like those that are seen on the hulls of ships, range. the seven seas.

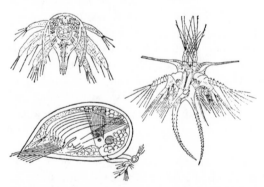

FIG. 26. Three larval stages of a stalked barnacle (*Lepas*). Upper left, newly hatched nauplius. Right, metanauplius. Lower left, cypris stage. All much enlarged. After Groom and Claus.

Barnacles of the genus *Chelonibia* are found on the shells of sea turtles, a location for which they are structurally well adapted. Others are found attached only to whales. The late Mr. Ira Cornwall observed that these species accommodated themselves most wonderfully to the ten thousand-mile voyages indulged in by their mighty hosts, during which the whales journey from their breeding ground in the equatorial seas to their summer feeding grounds in the shadow of the Poles. To cope with the extremes of environment confronting the animals in the course of the whales' migration—especially the sojourn in tropic seas—certain of the whale barnacles

FIG. 27. Three stalked barnacles, *Conchoderma auritum*, sealed on a whale barnacle *Coronula diadema*, in turn attached to a piece of whale skin. About natural size.

of the genus *Coronula* (Fig. 27) possess the largest and most highly developed gills, or branchiae, of any cirripeds known. As Mr. Cornwall explained, "It is well known that the warm water of the tropical seas contains less oxygen than the cooler water of the northern and southern oceans; also the increase of temperature causes an increase of the rate of metabolism, and a consequent greater demand for oxygen. The combination of these two factors would explain the great development of the branchiae of the barnacles."

And how differently do the several species of whale barnacles attach themselves to their host! *Coronula reginae,* with very few exceptions, is found on the lips and the front edge of the flippers; *Coronula diadema,* in heavy masses on the throat and corrugated belly. *Coronula reginae* first embeds itself below the surface of the skin, with only the hood projecting above it. As the shell grows, the skin is forced back and eventually about a third of the shell is exposed. Another barnacle, also found on whales, is so attached to the flippers and flukes that its opening faces backward when the whale is in motion. This barnacle has been reported as occurring on porpoises also. The rarest of the whale barnacles in American collections is a small, tubular, storied-looking affair, *Tubicinella major*. It is found on the upper jaw, on the forehead, and over the eye of the southern right whale. *Stomatolepas,* as the name indicates, is found embedded in the mucous membrance of the gullet of sea turtles. *Platylepas* lives embedded in the skin of turtles and in that of manatees, sea snakes, and fishes as well.

As is well known, barnacles attach themselves to ships. In the course of a study made some years ago of the bottoms of about 250 ships calling at Atlantic coast ports of the United States, not less than sixteen species of barnacles were listed. They are among the organisms that contribute most toward the fouling of ships; and they have the added disadvantage from the mariner's standpoint, that their shells remain even after they die and can be removed only when the vessel is docked and scraped. Softer animals and seaweeds tend to die and rot off when moved from warm to cold or from fresh to salt water or vice versa.

According to the United States Bureau of Fisheries, untreated or neglected ships have been found to carry more than one hundred tons of fouling material, and in some instances more than three hundred tons. Before the protection afforded by modern anti-fouling compositions was available, fouling was found to diminish the speed of a vessel as much as fifty percent and increase the time required for a voyage from ten to fifty percent; it caused an increase of fuel consumption, with corresponding wear and tear on the machinery, and necessitated frequent docking. A Chinese freighter that put into Charleston early in 1964 had just this experience.

Docked for overhaul, she was found to be thickly encrusted with oysters upwards of four inches in length. These, in turn, were covered with sessile barnacles of all sizes. The ship's speed, the captain said, had been slowed from a normal eleven to twelve knots to about six; a voyage that otherwise would have been completed in forty-five days took two months. The heavy fouling undoubtedly took place while the ship lay idle for five months in Taipei Harbor. Passing through the fresh water of the Panama Canal apparently had little or no effect on either the barnacles or the oysters.

Coatings employed by the Navy in the Second World War have been used extensively on ships since then and when used have rendered it virtually unnecessary to make allowance for fouling in estimating fuel requirements and maintenance costs.

The hulls of ships treated with hot plastic coatings have remained practically clean for periods as long as twenty-eight months. The cost today for docking, scraping, and painting or plastic coating the hull of a vessel such as the Queen Elizabeth, with more than three acres of underwater surface, runs to as much as $100,000. Crustaceans do take an uncounted toll of ships and shippers! And the fouling of ships still must be a matter of some concern for we have heard that fair success is attending an attempt to develop an antibiotic or a fouling inhibitor from Sargassum weed. It has been conservatively estimated that thirty years ago the annual cost of fouling to the shipping industry of our country amounted to more than $100,000,000. I have been told that today's figure, with improved coatings, stands at about the same figure, even though there are more ships, more traffic, and higher costs.

But barnacles have their uses as well as their drawbacks from man's point of view. In Chile, where a common species grows to a prodigious size (for a barnacle)—nine inches in length and several inches across—the meat of this shrimp relative is an important article of food (Fig. 28). It is considered quite a delicacy and is much sought after as an ingredient to soups and chowders. The flavor—all its own—of this barnacle soup, as I can attest, is equal to that of the best clam chowder, while the flesh is more palatable than clam meat. In Japan a small species of barnacle is cultivated on stakes, from which it is scraped off and used as fertilizer.

FIG. 28. A cluster of large sessile barnacles, *Balanus psittacus* (x 1/5).

One of the strangest phenomena about some species of barnacles is that the males are dwarfs. The great majority of Cirripedia are hermaphroditic; but two genera, *Scalpellum* and *Ibla*, have dwarf males comparable to those known in some deep-sea fishes and in certain other crustaceans. These males are often without appreciable structure, and probably all are short-lived. Some of them are attached to hermaphroditic individuals and so seem to be "complemental males," as apparently they are not altogether necessary in the perpetuation of the species. When attached to purely female individuals, however, the dwarf males must be of some use. Such males are structurally more developed—having something of an alimentary tract—and are able to carry on a life of greater duration, but scarcely of greater independence than "complemental males," as they are confined to the mantle cavity of the female and dependent on her bounty for existence.

Before concluding our study of Cirripedia, something should be said of Rhizocephala, of which little more than mention has been made so far. In a number of species rhizocephalids rank with the stalked as well as sessile barnacles, but they are poor relations of a sort, having become such abject parasites as not to be recognizable as barnacles, or even as crustaceans, if it were not for their life history. The rhizocephalids prey on other crustaceans only. Found parasitic almost exclusively on decapod Crustacea, the full-grown rhizocephalid appears superficially little more than a tumorous growth attached to the underside of the abdomen of the host.

An adult rhizocephalid is a mere envelope of thin chitin: it shows no trace of segmentation, appendages, or an alimentary tract. Its visceral mass contains reproductive organs (usually male and female in one animal), and is nourished by a threadlike absorptive root system which penetrates the body of its host in all directions. Its effect on male decapod hosts is profound, resulting in an apparent unsexing. The male crabs, particularly, when infested with rhizocephalids, tend to take on the secondary female characters of their kind, most noticeably the broader abdomen of the female (Fig. 29).

But stranger than its effect on its host's structure is the life history of the rhizocephalid. Hatching out usually as a nauplius and transforming into a cypris stage, like any normal barnacle, it settles down usually on

FIG. 29. Adult rhizocephalids parasitic on the abdomen of a hermit crab, a burrowing shrimp, and a crab. After Smith.

some decapod host. It is selective, however, in its choice of hosts. Some forms will infest only one species of crustacean. The larva settles down on its specific host wherever it can find lodgment, though, seldom, if ever, on the abdomen, where the adult rhizocephalid is found. Probably burrowing downward at the base of a hair or seta through the covering of a newly molted decapod, the larva undergoes some remarkable changes in order to work its way through the body of its host and finally, in an unexplained manner, to find lodgment above the abdominal wall. Here it begins to send out rootlike processes, which cause degeneration of the body wall of the host. An opening is formed through which, at the time of one of the molts of the host, the mass of the rhizo-cephalid takes up its accustomed external position. The parasite then proceeds to absorb the vital fluids of the crustacean which carries it and to produce new individuals of its kind, which, in their turn, will infest other crustaceans.

III. The Family Album

Part II
The Subclass Malacostraca

This subclass contains the lobsters, crabs, and shrimps. It contains also many other kinds of crustaceans—more than twice as many as all the other subclasses of Crustacea put together, so that we may expect to find quite a number of strange forms in this immediate family circle of the familiar decapods. But we have at least one reliable touchstone by which to test any true malacostracan. That is the possession of nineteen body segments. In the entire subclass, the most primitive of its superorders—the Leptostraca—is, by the count of plus-one, an exception to the "nineteen segment" rule. All the others conform.

Taking in so many of the better-known and more familiar crustaceans, the Malacostraca are here dealt with by order and superorder, in greater detail than any of the preceding seven subclasses.

Superorder Leptostraca*
Order Nebaliacea

A good malacostracan from head to toe, representative

---

* Interchangeably with, or in place of Leptostraca, some authors use Phyllocarida, but Leptostraca is preferred here.

of the Leptostraca is *Nebalia bipes* (Fig. 30), differing from all the rest only by the tip of its tail, for in its tail lies its distinguishing character and the evidence of its relationship to lower orders of Crustacea. While in all other Malacostraca the abdomen is made up of six somites, in the Leptostraca it includes seven, and the telson or tailpiece is forked in a manner reminiscent of the Branchiopoda. Thus the total number of somites in

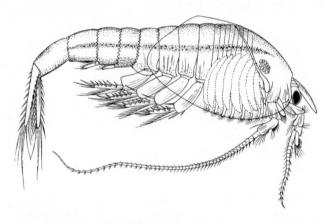

FIG. 30. Female *Nebalia bipes,* showing the forked telson and movable rostrum (x 9). After Sars.

the Leptostraca is twenty instead of nineteen and so they tend, however slightly, toward the variability in number of somites that is a character of lower orders. The carapace of the Leptostraca likewise differs from that of the rest of the Malacostraca that possess one, for it is hinged on the mid-dorsal line and is provided with an adductor muscle to draw the two halves together. The rostrum is hinged and movable and when bent down closes the anterior gape of the carapace for all the world like the snap lid on a syrup pot. No doubt this novel shield functions at times to better protect the ova, which are carried by the female in a sort of loose basket formed by the thoracic legs.

The Leptostraca are wholly without fresh-water representatives so far as known. Though mostly shallow-water forms, at least one species, the blind *Nebalia typhlops,* ranges the intermediate depths of the ocean, from five hundred to seven hundred fifty fathoms down, where it feeds on smaller organisms. Except for *Nebalia typhlops,* the Leptostraca are largely, if not wholly, detritus feeders—stirring up the sea bottom in search of food— and at times scavengers; for a favorite way of securing them in the Dry Tortugas, Florida, is by putting out partly-cleaned lobster shells as bait, which as soon as the adhering flesh begins to decay literally swarm with *Nebalia.* Temperature seems to affect but little their life processes. Most Leptostraca measure between three-sixteenths and three-quarters of an inch in length, but the giant among them, *Nebaliopsis typica,* measures more than an inch and a half.

Superorder Hoplocarida
Order Stomatopoda

The stomatopods, or "Squillas," comprise a small and homogeneous group, rather closely adhering to type. Their most characteristic features are their "jackknife" claws, so like those of our common garden mantis that they are usually known as mantis shrimps wherever English is spoken; the relatively large and much flattened abdomen; and the small hinged rostrum the like of which is not found among the Malacostraca outside of the Leptostraca. Despite their highly specialized appearance the stomatopods in the light of recent studies seem to be rather closely related to Leptostraca; for that reason they are placed here second in the hierarchy of malacostracan superorders.

The eyes, as well as the antennules, of stomatopods are borne on movable "rings" or segments, a character so unusual among the Crustacea that it distinguishes these from all other members of the class. Also, the stomatopods are foot breathers in a more specific sense than are other crustaceans, for each of the pleopods or abdominal feet is largely a feathered respiratory organ and not an accessory to egg-carrying.

The stomatopod young are queer little creatures, as odd in their way as are the phyllosome larvae of the spiny lobster. As glassy as any phyllosome and as long-spined of carapace as anything afloat, these larvae are more or less planktonic, though the eggs are hatched in the shelter of some recess or hiding place.

Stomatopods are burrowers in mud or sand bottoms, or else they preempt the burrow of some other marine excavator; some live in the interstices of coral reefs. All seem to be most suitably adapted in form and color to the mode of life they lead. In the spinous armature and color of its telson (Fig. 31) one species mimics a tiny sea-urchin so closely that when it is hidden in its coral

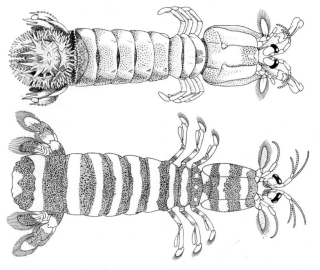

FIG. 31. Stomatopods, or mantis shrimps. Upper, *Gonodactylus guerinii* (after Brooks). Lower, *Lysiosquilla maculata* (after Kemp), showing extremes in ornamentation of telson.

burrow it has fooled even observant naturalists. At such times the spinous, urchin-resembling telson acts as a plug to the entrance of the burrow, effectively concealing the rest of the stomatopod within. The telsons of nearly all, if not all, stomatopods are very characteristically sculptured. Some indeed are unbelievably bizarre in appearance.

A stomatopod larva in season must be the ogre of all the other free-swimming crustacean young, for its formidable claws do not hesitate to seize anything, even creatures as large as itself. Such was the observation made by Dr. Marie V. Lebour in an aquarium of the Plymouth Marine Biological Laboratory in England.

Once one of 5 mm. was seen to catch a Upogebia larva nearly as long as itself (Fig. 32). For catching such a large animal the chelae come into play and hold the prey tightly between the two terminal joints. For some time it swam about holding its burden like a baby and beautifully balanced. When first captured the Upogebia was very lively, but soon subsided and died, apparently from intense pressure, but after about half an hour it was dropped and not eaten. Possibly it was too big and had exhausted the Squilla too much. It is certain, however, that the purpose of the chelae is for catching and holding the prey. The Squilla larva always goes towards the light and dances happily up and down with an eager alertness which suggests the constant excitement of capturing live food.

"Like father, like son," certainly applies to the stomatopods, for the adults are unquestionably despoilers of all other kinds of crustaceans. It is not without reason that the wicked and powerful claws of the larva, when fully grown, have earned their possessors the name of "split thumb" in Bermuda and in the West Indies. They

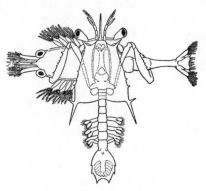

FIG. 32. A larval stomatopod with a captured larva of a burrowing shrimp, *Upogebia*. (x 15). After Lebour.

are the thugs of crustaceandom, hiding in their runs and warrens by day and consummating their murderous deeds under cover of darkness. Only exceptionally do we find them feeding by day. Carnivorous in a high degree, they will eat meat of all descriptions—portions of large crustaceans, crabs, fish, mollusks, worms. They prey upon all available species of shrimp and upon other stomatopods, for cannibalism is not beneath these "racketeers" of the seas and littoral zone. They are especially fond of their relatives when these are soft and toothsome, in the molting stage. The stomatopods like their soft-shelled crabs as well as you or I. Live fish they catch whenever they get the chance. Sea-anemones are good to eat and are much eaten by the peoples of the Mediterranean region, and some of the stomatopods of these same shores feast eagerly upon them too.

The sharp claws of stomatopods are quite obviously as serviceable for defense as for offense; and to these weapons can be added, if need be, the strong telson spines and the sharp armature of the uropods of all species, which can be lashed out on occasion in all directions by the especially flexible and loose-jointed body. But, as Wilhelm von Giesbrecht quite naturally inquired many years ago, against what enemies do these active marauders find it necessary to defend themselves? His inquiry revealed that though some observers had seen various sea-urchins in the act of devouring squillas, it would appear that the victims were either moribund or otherwise incapacitated specimens; for such as were in full possession of their faculties seemed to have little or no difficulty in tearing loose from any of the urchins' tube feet that may have become fastened to them. Octopuses are notorious enemies of crustaceans, particularly crabs, and in aquariums are nothing loath to tackle so porcupinelike a fellow as the stomatopod and to put him away, spines and all, in spite of the repeated blows they suffer in arms and body from the vicious claws and sharp tail spines of the struggling victim. Still, Professor Giesbrecht thought they were not to be reckoned as especial enemies of the active stomatopods.

The late William Keith Brooks wrote of stomatopods;

They are solitary in their habits, and I have never found two in the same burrow. They are pugnacious to an astonishing degree, and their fighting habits, as I have observed them in aquaria, are so fixed and constant that they must be constantly exercised by the animals when at home. When two specimens are placed together in an aquarium they at first appear to be unconscious of each other, but more careful examination will show that their eye stalks are in constant motion following each movement of the enemy. They soon assume a position in which they are face to face, although they may be on opposite sides of the aquarium, and the constant motion of their eye stalks shows how intently each movement is watched. Soon one attempts to get behind the other, but each such attempt is frustrated, until finally they are brought close together, face to face, and soon one springs suddenly upon the other and attempts to pinch some unprotected part. They then

spring apart and eye each other again to repeat
the attack at short intervals until one is disabled;
the other then springs upon him and soon tears him
limb from limb, disjointing all the free somites of
the body and tearing out and devouring the flesh.

Stomatopods and their larvae sometimes swarm in
incredible numbers. In the Indian Ocean a single trawl
haul has brought up as many as five hundred at a time.
During the Smithsonian-Roebling expedition to the
Great Antilles, off the west end of Cuba, the party's
motor cruiser one evening ran into such a swarm of
larvae that the sea was not only alive with them but
was like a thick soup. During migrations in the Chesapeake Bay area it has been observed that fish had taste
for nothing else. Unfortunately for fishermen, crustacean
swarms and migrations are difficult to predict.

Superorder Syncarida
Orders Anaspidacea and Bathynellacea

In 1865 two generically distinct but unmistakable
crustacean fossils were described from the coal-measures
of Illinois. For twenty years palaeontologists and carcinologists puzzled over their placement in the scheme of
things crustacean, until in 1886 A. S. Packard became
convinced they belonged to one group, hitherto unde-
fined. Appropriately, he named this group Syncarida.
Other closely related fossil genera were subsequently
discovered.

It is doubtful that Packard or his contemporaries ever
thought that a living syncarid might exist. But one was
discovered in 1893. It was given the name *Anaspides
tasmaniae* (Fig. 33). It is found only in the mountain
lakes and streams of southern and western Tasmania, at
elevations of from two thousand to four thousand feet. A
prime condition of its occurrence is ice cold water of
absolute clarity.

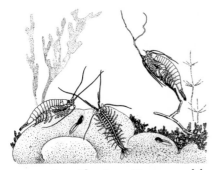

FIG. 33. *Anaspides tasmaniae*, on a lake bottom. Adapted from various authors.

Anaspides is the largest of the syncarids, attaining a length of almost two inches. There are three other groups of Anaspidacea, two of which, like *Anaspides tasmaniae*, are restricted to Tasmania; the other—*Koonunga cursor* —is found only in southeastern Australia.

The Syncarida, as typified by *Anaspides*, are among the most simply organized and most generalized in structure of the Malacostraca. In one character or another all show some resemblance to another Malacostracan group: in segmentation of body and lack of carapace they might pass for amphipods or isopods; the organs of equilibration or statocysts in the basal joints of the biramous antennules are characteristic of the decapods; in common with many euphausiids, their relatively few eggs are shed directly in the water and receive no care. Lastly, certain features of their internal anatomy are not unlike corresponding ones in the stomatopods.

Bathynella natans was described from a single specimen from a well in Prague, Czechoslovakia, in 1882, but its syncarid affinities were not established until three decades later, when a number of specimens were discovered in a spring at Basel, Switzerland. After that, at intervals of a few years and often in successive years the species was noted in other wells in Basel and elsewhere in Switzerland. An enthusiastic search by biologists—in Germany in particular—produced numerous new records; in 1925 some of these generally obscure little fellows were detected in the water mains of Oefingen, and more recently, in the upper and lower Rhine country. *Bathynella natans* has also been reported from England, Hungary, and the Balkan states.

Farther afield investigators have turned up close to thirty species of Bathynellacea which have been placed in six genera. They are virtually world-wide in their distribution—although none has yet been discovered in North America. Japanese zoologists have accounted for a third of the known species, which belong to three of the established genera.

Of all these genera of high or low degree, *Parabathynella malaya* has for me the greatest sentimental appeal—irrespective of its scientific importance. For it was described by the grand old man of carcinological history—George Ossian Sars—in his 89th year. This crustacean was noticed in a stream in Assam, India. Attempts to classify it were unsuccessful, so it finally was forwarded to Sars. Cedric Dover, who sent it on, later remarked of Sars' published description; "The paper in which this novelty was given the name *Parabathynella malaya* must be regarded, I think, as one of the smaller classics of zoology. It was written in a foreign language, and published without the benefit of revision by the author, or adequate editorial attention; but it is a model of clarity, unpretentiousness and deductive power, which ... [Sars] himself felt was his most important single contribution to carcinology.... Professor Sars died shortly after its completion."

The bathynellids as a rule are stenotherms, cold water animals. For *Bathynella natans,* the most favorable range lies between 46 or 47 and 50 degrees. *Anaspides* appears to tolerate a somewhat greater range—in the summertime 42 to about 58 degrees Fahrenheit, and close to freezing temperatures during the Tasmanian winters. The bathynellids are completely blind, largely colorless, subterranean water-dwelling forms. They turn up at times in borings, in springs, and in wells tapping ground waters. Occasionally they may swim short stretches, but most of the time they spend crawling over the bottom, carefully feeling about for the microscopic, unicellular rhizopod protozoans upon which they are known to feed. Little else is known of their diet. *Anaspides*, it has been discovered, is predaceous, eating other small invertebrates. It also is equipped to indulge in filter feeding.

Superorder Pancarida
Order Thermosbaenacea

Thermosbaena mirabilis Monod (Fig. 34) was first collected in 1923, from a shallow hot spring in the vicinity of the ruins of an old Roman bath near Tunis, North Africa. So strange was it and so different from all other known crustaceans that not until 1927 was it placed in the then current classificatory scheme as a new order, Thermosbaenacea, close to the Mysidacea. A small animal scarcely more than an eighth of an inch in length, it was first thought to be a larva or some other juvenile form of an unknown crustacean. The body of *Thermosbaena* is short and stubby, and the body regions are scarcely to be distinguished one from another without close examination. No trace of eyes or eye stalks has been found, and all the appendages are on quite a simplified or primitive plan.

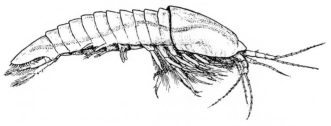

FIG. 34. *Thermosbaena mirabilis* Monod (x 25). After Bruun.

This discovery led to a re-examination of the type locality and other springs in the area and to study of its ecology. Between 1949 and 1953 three closely related species were found, two in the slightly brackish waters in a cave on the Adriatic shore in Italy and in a cave in Dubrovnik, Yugoslavia, and another in a fresh water cave in Tuscany. No other representative of the order has since been found. Considered generically distinct from *Thermosbaena*, these species were gathered into one genus, *Monodella*.

In common with *Thermosbaena*, the Monodellas—some of which grow to be as long as three-sixteenths of an inch—have a carapace which covers three thoracic segments and forms a dorsal marsupium, the like of which occurs in no other malacostracan. This characteristic plus the fact that in these two genera the female genital openings are on the seventh somite (rather than on the sixth as in other Malacostraca) called for the setting up of a new superorder, the Pancarida.

These little blind crustaceans live interstitially in ground water and are undoubtedly detritus feeders; *Thermosbaena* feeds also upon the algae of the Tunisian hot springs.

Thermosbaena mirabilis is the only pancaridan living in hot springs. In this thermal environment it appears to thrive—though the temperature fluctuates from about 98° F. to around 118° F. It becomes moribund if the temperature cools to 95°. The monodellas like to play it cool—the waters in caves in which they were found do not exceed 55 to 60° F.

Superorder Peracarida
Order Spelaeogriphacea

This is one of the most recently established (1957) of the six peracaridean orders. It was based on a single small, quarter- to a third-inch long organism, a shrimp-like, blind, transparent crustacean of which a number were discovered in a pool within a cave on Table Mountain, Capetown, South Africa. These bear some resemblance to the *Thermosbaenacea*, but whereas the brood pouch in the Pancarida is formed by the carapace and so is dorsal, that of *Spelaeogriphus* in common with all other peracaridan orders is ventral and formed of plates developed on some of the thoracic limbs. Five pairs of such overlapping plates form the brood pouch of *Spelaeogriphus*, in which its relatively large eggs are incubated. The Spelaeogriphacea differ from all other peracaridans in having vesicular, oval gills attached to three pairs of its thoracic legs, the fifth, sixth, and seventh. Regrettably, little or nothing has so far been developed regarding the life history, biology or internal anatomy of this little animal.

Order Mysidacea

Of the six orders comprising the superorder Peracarida, the second, Mysidacea, divides honors with the copepods and ostracods as a food for marine animals in all the oceans and in many of the lakes and smaller bodies of water in the Northern Hemisphere. Occurring in incalculable numbers, the mysids are small but prolific— although some grow to amazing size. The food of the Great Lakes fishes sold as chubs (more than nineteen million pounds annually) is ninety-five percent crustacean, virtually all of which is accounted, singly or together, by *Mysis relicta* and the fresh-water amphipod, *Pontoporeia*. In smaller chubs the food, according to season, consists of 38 to 56 percent copepods, 18 to 24 percent Cladocera, and 18 to 52 percent other zooplankton.

"Opossum shrimp" is the vernacular name of the order Mysidacea, inspired by the brood pouch (Fig. 35) formed by specially developed plates on the inner sides of the thoracic feet of the female. In this the eggs are hatched and the young sheltered until they can strike

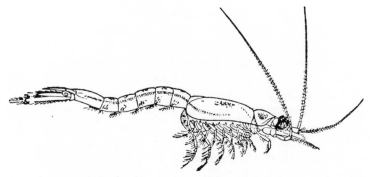

FIG. 35. A fresh-water opossum shrimp, *Mysis relicta*. The brood pouch shows between the thoracic feet. After Sars.

out for themselves with a full complement of well-developed appendages. The possession of such an incubative arrangement by the female is one of the distinguishing characters shared in common by all good peracaridans.

The Mysidacea, with the exception of a few rare forms, are without gills as we know them in the higher Crustacea, and even in these exceptional forms the gills are but rudimentary. Furthermore, the mysidacean carapace fails to unite dorsally with at least the last four thoracic somites.

The filamentous schizopods (or split feet) of the mysids are their means of locomotion and respiration; and they also produce a current in the water which wafts and drives the finer detritus, their food, within reach of the mouth and its accessory appendages.

Mysids (Fig. 36) seem never to have become parasites, though they themselves are much plagued by isopods, which seem to leave untouched scarcely any group of marine animals whatsoever except such as are too small to furnish them a foothold or nourishment. Protozoan colonies have also been found infesting certain species of mysids. On the other hand, mysids probably are largely scavengers. Though their appendages and mouth parts are fashioned for filter feeding, their strong mandibles enable them to chew up and eat larger organisms

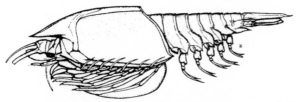

FIG. 36. *Gnathophausia ingens,* the largest known mysid shrimp. From the tropical Pacific, almost 1½ miles down. Grows to be nearly fourteen inches in length. From Brinton.

and food masses caught by their legs. Thus a lot of scavenged food is made available to the larger forms of aquatic life in the form of mysids.

Order Cumacea

Next among the orders of the superorder Peracarida are "some little wonders and queer blunders," the Cumacea, so odd and characteristic of build—and, one is apt to feel, of personality—that once you have made the acquaintance of one or two of them you will forever after be able to recognize them in any gathering of Crustacea. With a carapace that is apparently too large for them (yet fails to protect the whole of the thorax) and a slender, feeble looking abdomen that seems much too small, their little misshapen bodies are quite unforgettable. But nature has her plans and purposes, though most of them are yet unknown to us. What strikes us as a seeming lack of balance between the fore and hinder parts of the body is no doubt the most efficient combination that could be contrived to facilitate plowing through the mud and detritus in which many cumaceans live. We do know that the abdomen is most freely movable. The animal can reach all parts of its body with the forked end of its tail. In spite of messy surroundings it is a cleanly little beggar, forever furbishing up one or another part of its external anatomy with the mobile tail, giving special attention to the food-getting appendages, which need frequent cleansing to work at full efficiency.

Small and inconspicuous as these retiring burrowers are, they sometimes occur in such vast numbers as to become an important source of food for fishes. On such occasions the males of a number of species tend to swarm at the surface, especially at night. The male is by far the more active sex and is better provided with pleopods than the female and so better fitted for swimming.

Cumacea are found in every part of the ocean, and as far north as deep-water exploration has been instituted these peculiar Crustacea are plentiful. Indeed, in the Arctic Ocean they seem to reach their maximum development, the huge *Diastylis goodsiri* (Fig. 37) being more than an inch in length.

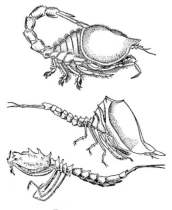

FIG. 37. Representative Cumacea. Upper, the giant *Diastylis goodsiri*, cleaning carapace with the tip of its tail (x ½). Middle, *Ceratocuma horrida*, adult male (x 3½). Lower, *Campylaspis vitrea*, young female (x 3½). After Sars and Calman.

A further peculiarity of this order noticeable enough to merit comment is its sessile eyes, which are drawn so closely together that they merge into one, giving the Cumacea a cyclopean appearance.

Order Tanaidacea

Introductory, as it were, to the two final orders comprising the Peracarida, we have a small yet well-marked

FIG. 38. Tanaids. *Sphyrapus anomalus*, male, and *Tanais tomentosus*, female (x 6), carrying eggs. After Sars.

group, the Tanaidacea (Fig. 38). The chief character separating this order from the isopods is the possession of a carapace which coalesces dorsally with the first two thoracic somites, overhanging laterally to form a branchial cavity on either side. Their eyes are a compromise between those of the stalk- and the sessile-eyed peracarids, inasmuch as those species in which the eyes are not wanting altogether usually have them on little immovable processes on the head, which seem to be analogous with the ocular peduncles of the mysids.

Most of the more familiar Tanaidacea—if we may call familiar, creatures which most of us will never see—are quite small. Not much is known of their mode of life, but certain of them live in the mud of the littoral zone or hide away among algae, hydroids, and the like. Certain bottom-dwelling tanaids may spin themselves little tangles of thread, within which to conceal themselves, or else fabricate a tube from their secretions, which becomes encrusted with bottom materials, camouflaging it. An American species, *Tanais robustus,* has, I think, the most peculiar place of abode of all the members of the "tribe." This species inhabits minute tubes in the crevices between the scales of a turtle's (*Thalassochelys caretta*) carapace.

Not all of these creatures restrict themselves to shallow water, for during the Danish Deep-Sea Expedition in 1950-52, four specimens of *Neotanais* were brought up from a depth of forty-five hundred fathoms in the Kermadec Trench off New Zealand. The largest of these was nearly five-eighths of an inch long. A specimen of *Herpotanais* was taken in the same waters, but from a depth of thirty-nine hundred fathoms. This measured nearly an inch long and so is the largest known tanaid.

Orders Isopoda and Amphipoda

For the first time since we took leave of the barnacles we meet crustaceans of which most of us have probably heard before; namely the Isopoda, to which belong the better-known wood-lice, pill-bugs, or sow bugs, found in damp places, and the Amphipoda, which include the sandhoppers, or sand or beach fleas, with which most visitors to the seashore are familiar. Both orders contain, in addition, many salt- and fresh-water forms not so well known.

But how is one to tell an amphipod from an isopod? The two are so much alike and so much akin that only a combination of rather detailed characteristics serve as a sure means of distinguishing them. For a superficial—though by no means universal—rule, one might say that the isopods are depressed, that is, flattened from above and below, whereas the amphipods are compressed—flattened from side to side. Also, isopods generally lack claws, whereas all amphipods have them.

In alluding to the amphipods, Stebbing referred to them as the "many twinkling feet." To examine their many and diverse appendages is to discover that they seem to carry about with them almost as many tools as the proverbial plumber. In one and the same animal the different appendages are adapted to such various uses as feeling, biting, culling, holding, back brushing, swimming, jumping, and what not.

"Among the Amphipoda," to quote Dr. Stebbing again, "there are a few species armed with strictly defensive spines, but otherwise they are of all the Malacostraca the most absolutely and universally peaceable towards mankind, never inflicting upon him any personal injury whatever." The same might be said of the amphipods' attitude toward animals other than man. They are primarily the most efficient scavengers of sea and shore, the multiplicity of them rendering them of more service in clearing up organic debris on all the world's shores than any other animals, even those much larger than themselves.

Perhaps the only great harm that can be charged to amphipods is that of destroying wooden harbor works. One species, *Chelura terebrans,* belongs to the great triumvirate of animals most destructive to wood immersed in salt water, the other two members of which are the molluscan shipworms and certain of the isopods, notably *Limnoria lignorum.* The amphipods are ever so much more preyed upon than preying, and only a few among them—like *Cyamus,* the whale louse—can be classed as at all parasitic.

Eighteen or so *Cyamus* species are known. As a rule they are host-specific—each to its own kind of host. Not often is more than one species reported from a given whale, but from a California gray whale killed by the Point Barrow Eskimos in 1954 numerous specimens of three species were collected. Two had previously been reported from this whale, but the third had not been seen since 1873!

The whale-lice leave the brood pouch of the parent as young adults and immediately dig in on the host with their sharp, hooked dactyls to avoid being carried away by the rush of water created by a whale in motion. There is no intervening free-swimming stage as with so many other Crustacea. One wonders how the cyamids get about, from whale to whale. Drs. D. E. Hurley and J. L. Mohr, who reported the triple infestation of the gray whale, suggested the transfer is accomplished by actual bodily contacts—between mother and young at birth and when nursing, in the mating season, at play, when feeding or traveling, or during an attack of one whale upon another. Thus an ordinarily host-specific crustacean could get onto an alien host on which it had no business to be. In Alaskan waters and the Bering Sea, ranges of the California gray and the bowhead overlap.

Despite their close identification with the whales, cyamids have been recovered from other marine mammals, notably dolphins, norwhales, and most recently, from a false killer whale in the Gulf of Mexico.

Amphipods form the bulk of the food of many animals, particularly fish, and several of the abundant pelagic species are said to form part of the crustacean diet of whales. Quite otherwise is it with the isopods. Many species are free-swimming scavengers like the amphipods; but no end of them are degenerate parasites, lacking face and figure to such an extent that they can scarce be distinguished from the most depraved rhizocephalid except by the locality of their attack upon the host species and by some minute but peculiar points of their internal anatomy. I refer especially to the bopyrids (Fig. 39) which become attached to the gills of shrimp or crab and cause there a characteristic and readily recognized malformation. Like other parasitic crustaceans which prey on members of their class higher in

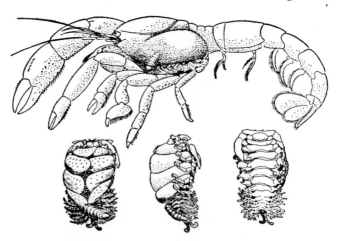

FIG. 39. A degenerate isopod, *Ione thoracica*. Female with a smaller male attached parasitizing the gill chamber of a burrowing shrimp. Below, ventral, lateral, and dorsal views of the female (x 4) with the small male in normal position. After Bonnier.

the scale than they, these isopod parasites in turn become parasitized. Also, among Isopoda as in some parasitic barnacles and copepods, we find repeated the phenomenon of dwarf males.

Many isopods without such characteristic degeneration of form are vicious enemies of fish. The cymothoids, for example, attach themselves to the sides of their unwilling hosts or find a foothold in their mouth cavities (Fig. 40). They must be pain-causing guests, for it is not safe to detach living ones—no matter how small—from their host with the bare hand. There have come to us a number of reports of painful "bites" that cymothoids have inflicted on the unwary by clamping the wondrously strong and wickedly sharp, sickle-shaped dactyls of their many legs into the unsuspecting palm or finger of the would-be collector.

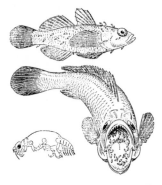

FIG. 40. Larvae of the isopod *Paragnathia formica* parasitizing the skin of a goby and the mouth of a connor. Lower left, an individual larva (x 3⅞). This species is parasitic only in its young stages. After Monod.

The young of these isopods just after hatching are worse than a pack of ravenous wolves in the way they assail the nearest fish in their search of a host on which to dwell and feed. Such lilliputian marine battles have, under favorable circumstances, been observed in tide pools, where the fish always seems to get the worst of it.

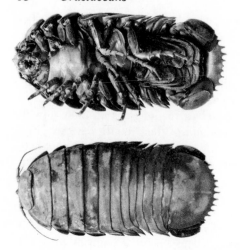

FIG. 41. The giant isopod, *Bathynomus giganteus*, ventral and dorsal views.

A striking form among the isopods is *Bathynomus giganteus* (Fig. 41), one of the giants. among crustaceans, growing to at least fourteen inches in length. The largest amphipod, *Alicella gigantea* (Fig. 42), is less than half the length of the largest known isopod. In tenuity of body other amphipods take first place. Often zoologically curious visitors to the U.S. National Museum ask to see the skeleton shrimp. They refer to the amphipod *Caprella* (Fig. 43), which for all its slender build and lack of edible meat is one of the better known of crustaceans. *Caprella* turns a ghostly white after being pickled for any length of time, but in life it is

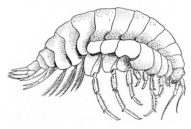

FIG. 42. Female of the amphipod, *Alicella gigantea* (x ½). After Chevreux.

among the most adaptable of animals in reproducing the color of its surroundings. Its bodily form is equally imitative of its usual habitat, and as a result of this capacity for mimicry *Caprella* is hard to find, even though it may occur in great numbers. Not without reason is it called "skeleton shrimp": dwelling among the finely branched seaweeds, bryozoa, and hydroids, in shape and posture and color it is for all the world like a short branch of any of these marine growths.

Do not think that the skeleton shrimps are the only mimics among the amphipods. Some of the plumper fellows, too, like the pelagic genus, *Mimonectes,* are no mean imitators. Except for an odd little tail, without which *Mimonectes* wouldn't be an amphipod, the resemblance of the large transparent body of one of these to a floating jellyfish is well-nigh perfect.

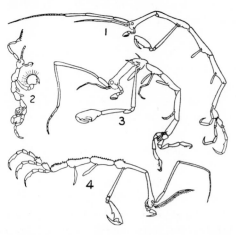

FIG. 43. Caprellid amphipods, skeleton shrimps, which in color, shape and posture mimic marine growths. 1, 2, and 4, *Caprella;* 3, *Dodecas.* Approximate magnification, Figs. 2, 3 (x 5); Figs. 1, 4 (x 3). After Mayer.

When one beholds the hordes of fish that subsist on amphipods alone, the mere number of these crustaceans in the world makes one marvel. Several pelagic amphipods form at times a very considerable part of the diet of the herring and the mackerel. And when the pelagic amphipods are plentiful, then does the Biscayan tunny fishery flourish; when the amphipod food supply falls off, just so surely does the fishery languish. Amphipods that frequent the sea bottom likewise supply much of the food of bottom-feeding fishes of the flounder tribe.

Certain birds also profit largely from the teeming numbers of amphipods. Mr. F. J. Stubbs calculated that in a square mile of sand on the Westmoreland coast of England there were, on an average, twenty amphipods inhabiting each square inch, and that the total weight of crustaceans for the area was seven hundred tons. He was surprised to observe that the only species of bird which seemed to feed on this particularly rich food supply was the black-headed gull.

The amphipods burrow in the sandy mud, making U-shaped passages about two inches in depth. Mr. Stubbs gives a graphic description of how the black-headed gull procures this crustacean food.

> The Gull stands in the water, and, holding its body horizontally, *dances* vigorously with alternate steps for a minute or more, but with no change of position. This action on the sand, possibly by filling up the burrows, alarms the crustaceans, which rise to the water and scatter in flight. As soon as they appear the bird stops its dance for a second or so, and, still remaining precisely in the same spot, snaps in the water at the swimming animals. On imitating the action with the tips of my fingers, and, of course, with the same result, I found that the crustaceans were readily detected by the sense of touch as they struggled to the water; and this suggested the possibility of the webs of the Gull's toes being used as tactile organs. The point is well worth consideration, for if established it would explain the presence of highly developed webs in birds which are addicted to wading but rarely use their feet in swimming.

Antarctic penguins also seem fond of amphipods. At Paradise Harbor in 1963, I saw them diving, duck-fashion, in the kelp along shore at low tide. Here a few sweeps with a dip net would bring up a number of sizeable amphipods but no other crustaceans. I did not examine any stomach contents, but there seemed to be nothing else here for these crustacean fanciers but amphipods.

Least known of the amphipods are the large bathypelagic species of which the nearly five inch long *Cystosoma magna* (Fig. 44) is one of the best known examples.

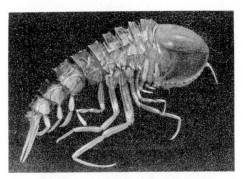

FIG. 44. *Cystosoma magna.* From Woltereck.

Superorder Eucarida
Order Euphausiacea

Men and whales alike, on purely selfish grounds, would put the two orders contained in the superorder Eucarida first in importance among Crustacea; for these two orders are our old friends the Decapoda, preferred of men, and the Euphausiacea, preferred of whales. But however much they may be strangers to his palate, the euphausiids are not unknown to man. No traveler on the Atlantic or Pacific Ocean who has leaned over the rail of his ship at night can have missed the sparkles of light in the waves turned back from the vessel's sides and in its wake. In the colder reaches these are the flashings of the tiny "lamps" ornamenting the bodies and appendages of euphausiids. For all of them except a single genus have organs capable of emitting light.

A euphausiid might be considered, in an evolutionary sense, a grownup mysid. It has a carapace which is fused dorsally with all the thoracic somites, and beneath which feather-like gills show plainly. As in the mysid, the outer branches of all the thoracic appendages are especially developed for swimming, giving the legs the characteristic split-foot appearance. Euphausiids may be found the world over, but only in salt and brackish waters. Like other Crustacea, they have their giant form. In this order, it is the three and three quarters inch long *Thysanopoda cornuta* (Fig. 45) that the Scripps Institution brought up in its midwater trawling in the southeastern part of the Gulf of Alaska. This species lives at depths ranging from eleven hundred to six thousand fathoms where the water at the lower level would freeze were it not salt. *Thysanopoda cornuta* occurs also in the deeper waters of the Atlantic and Indian Oceans but there in size falls far short of its Alaskan brethren.

At least two species of the euphausiids constitute the major part of the diet of the Antarctic whales. A moderate-sized blue whale tucks a mere two or three tons of them under his waistline at a meal! And whales

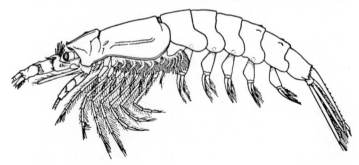

FIG. 45. *Thysanopoda cornuta*, largest known euphausiid. From Brinton.

are only one of the many kinds of animals that feast on this rich and plentiful food; for the seals and the penguins and petrels of these southern seas are largely, if not wholly, dependent on the euphausiids. In the North Atlantic *Meganyctiphanes* is the prime whale food, and the finback is at times literally packed with them. The finback is but one kind among a number of the whales that eat euphausiids, and *Meganyctiphanes* is but one among a number of kinds of euphausiids eaten by whales.

Order Decapoda

Topping the crustacean scheme of things are the Decapoda, subdivided into two major groups—the Natantia, or swimmers (best described as the true shrimps or prawns), and the Reptantia, or crawlers (crayfishes, lobsters, crabs, and their allies). As the name Decapoda implies, the members of this order are ten-footed. They may be readily distinguished by this character and by the well-developed carapace which covers the united head and thorax. It is true that in some crablike forms—the lithodid and the porcellanid crabs—the hind legs are small and sometimes tucked in under the edges of the carapace so that their possessors appear to be eight-legged rather than ten-legged; and in some of the lesser known shrimps one of the five pairs of thoracic legs may be suppressed; but all in all the build of a decapod is so unmistakably shrimplike or crablike that we have no hesitation about its proper classification.

In only one group of decapods, the peneid shrimps, do the young hatch out in a nauplius stage, for all the world like a barnacle or copepod nauplius; and only in this same group, also, do the females deposit their eggs instead of carrying them until they hatch.

No decapods except the peneids hatch out of the egg at a stage earlier than a zoea, and a few species leave the egg not so very unlike their adult forms. The spiny lobsters and the shovel-nosed or Spanish lobsters are unique in hatching out in a form quite unknown in other Crustacea. This form is called the phyllosoma-larva or "glass" shrimp, so thin, flat, and transparent is it (Fig. 46). Swimming in its native element, it just cannot be seen by human eyes. Only in a bucket of water in which the sun is shining can its presence be detected by virtue of the shadow it casts, which is due to the difference of the refractive powers of the phyllosome from that of the surrounding water. Out of water, at the bottom of one's net, it appears as a bit of crumpled gelatine, so easily does it "kink" when removed from its supporting medium. The little phyllosome passes through a dozen or two larval stages which give no hint at all of its adult form. Suddenly it transforms into a tiny, smooth, nonspiny lobsterlike being, itself so unlike the adult that it remained for a long time unassociated ın the scientist's mind with the spiny lobster. Finally it acquires its familiar adult form.

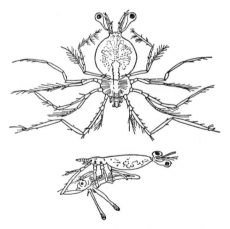

FIG. 46. Phyllosome larva of the English rock or spiny lobster (*Palinurus elephas*) (x 7). Upper, dorsal view. Lower, larva capturing a baby angler fish. After Lebour.

To illustrate the life history of a typical reptant deca-pod, we can do no better than make use of portions of Dr. O. W. Hyman's vivid account of that of the fiddler crab, *"Adventures in the Life of a Fiddler Crab"*:

> Hatching always occurs just at dusk—that is, be-tween 7 and 8 o'clock. The mother crab comes down to the water's edge and fans her abdomen back and forth to aerate the eggs as usual. If the embryos are ready to hatch, however, the little larvae burst out of the egg shells and at each forward flirt of the abdomen a small spray of young larvae is shot forward into the water.

The young crab, or zoea, thus catapulted from the shelter of its mother's abdomen, measures only a mil-limeter in length when fully extended; and as in swim-ming the body is bent double, the swiftly moving larva is only about half a millimeter in length and the same in width (Fig. 47). When the zoea bursts from its

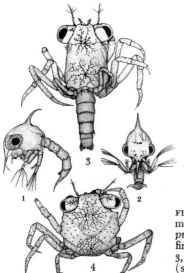

FIG. 47. Stages in the develop-ment of the fiddler crab (*Uca pugilator*). 1, side view of the first zoea. 2, front view of same. 3, megalops. 4, first crab stage (some legs lost). After Hyman.

eggshell it at once swims to the surface of the water, where it finds conditions that give it a chance to survive. But it is well that the brood is hatched at dusk and has all night to be scattered by the tide before the young members enter upon the adventures of their first day.

The zoea begins to feed upon the smaller of its countless companions at once and for the next four or five days the mouth parts are catching, crushing, and swallowing tiny animals and plants. As a result of this feeding the zoea begins to grow. Its inelastic chitin coat soon becomes too small. A new covering of larger size is formed beneath the old. For a short time now the zoea becomes motionless and sinks toward the bottom. The old coat then splits along the back at the place where the abdomen joins the cephalo-thorax. The zoea first pushes its body through the slit, and then draws its abdomen and appendages from their old sheaths. This is the first molt. The zoea which emerges is somewhat different from the first hatched zoea and is called the second zoea. The molting period is a perilous time in the life of the zoea. The larva is quite helpless, but fortunately it is almost invisible against the sandy or shelly bottom on which the molt generally occurs.

In the "sand fiddler" studied by Hyman there are zoeal molts at about weekly intervals—four in all, and marked increase in size is noted after each molt. The fourth zoea is just twice as long as the first. The fifth "is no longer the graceful, restless, palpitating form of larva that suggested the name Zoea, 'Life,' to describe it. The body is so heavy that the maxillipeds can only keep it at the surface for short periods. Most of its life is spent drifting along near the bottom."

The last zoeal molt takes place when the animal has been living at sea a little over a month. Of the hundreds of young hatched by one female only a score or so will have survived through this molt, which marks the transition to a new larval stage.

The larva that stretches itself after jerking loose its last attachments to the zoeal skin could hardly be recognized as derived from a zoea—even the changed zoea of the fifth stage. As a matter of fact, it was described by earlier naturalists as an entirely separate genus and called *Megalops,* from its large and prominent eyes. This name has been retained to describe this stage in the larval history, just as pupa describes the second stage in the larval history of the butterflies. The *Megalops* is a larva far different from a pupa, however. Instead of being a motionless, sluggish creature it is a powerfully swimming corsair of the ocean's surface.

... It is easily seen as it darts about the surface. The sensory organs are now well developed. The eyes are large and well formed.... the animal swims about in any direction and can change direction quickly and accurately. It is no longer guided in its movement solely by its reaction to light, but is independent of this tropism and seeks its prey at all depths. It remains at the surface most of the time, however, as food is most abundant there.... The animal can hear, in the sense that its delicate hairs perceive the vibrations in the water just as the ears of higher animals record the sound waves of the air. These "hearing" hairs are especially located on the antennae and antennules....

The shape of the body is now more that of a crab than that of a zoea, but in some respects it is intermediate between the two. The spines of the zoeal carapace are lost and the body is somewhat flattened from above and below. However, it is still considerably longer than broad and in this respect resembles somewhat the body of a shrimp. In fact the megalops may be said in general to have the body of a shrimp or crayfish with the legs of a crab. The abdomen is like that of the crayfish and in swimming is carried extended straight out behind. When the animal comes to rest, however, it is folded under the body and the megalops then looks very much like a tiny crab. . . .

The megalops swims about for nearly a month. Unlike the zoea it does not go through a series of molts during this time, although it undergoes considerable internal development. After some three or four weeks of its roving existence these internal changes begin to affect its swimming powers. The swimmerets or pleopods begin to shrivel up slightly. After this begins the megalops is glad to find some convenient place to cling and hide. . . . This loss of the power of the pleopods for swimming marks the end of the sea life and adventures of the larva. When these organs lose their function it will never again be able to swim.

After perhaps a week in its shelter the megalops molts, and out of the megalops shell crawls what is unquestionably a crab, though hardly recognizable yet as a fiddler. After four or more molts in the crab stage the young crab begins to develop secondary sex characters distinguishing the male from the female.

The young crab after this lives just like the adult. It gets its food from the sand on the beach, digs its burrow between the tide lines, comes out and feeds when the tide is falling, and hides in its burrow when the tide is coming in. It continues to grow, and as it grows continues to molt time after time. Of course, as the crab grows larger it digs a deeper and larger burrow. . . .

When the weather begins to get cold in the late autumn all the crabs on the beach crawl into their burrows for the winter hibernation. The unlucky larvae and little crabs that are not yet strong enough to dig their burrows perish of exposure during the first cold weather. All during the winter the crabs remain buried. . . .

As soon as the first warm weather comes in spring all the little fiddlers become lively again and dig themselves out. Some of the young crabs of the preceding summer may have become sexually mature by this time and by early April they lay their eggs, and soon the sounds and adjacent sea are receiving new swarms of delicate, active zoeas, setting out upon the great adventures through which every fiddler crab must pass in its youth.

But after all, what are youthful adventures compared to those of a more mature age? The sand fiddlers are agile runners, but a man can easily overtake them. As a protection from their enemies they rely in the main upon their burrows. These are dug along the beach just below the high-tide line and extend downward a foot or more at a very steep angle. When the tide comes in the crabs crawl into their burrows, and the beating of the wavelets soon stops their doors with sand. When the tide begins to ebb and leaves the beach, now all wet, the fiddlers dig themselves out again. The excavated sand is gathered in wet balls and distributed along the beach at a distance of about six or eight inches from the openings of the burrows. It is to be expected that the next time the fiddler enters his burrow he will be in a hurry and want a clear road. After he has made sure of his means of retreat, he joins his companions at the water's edge.

Each wavelet of the receding tide casts up on the beach a tiny "windrow" of sand. There is much more than sand in this "windrow," however. Among the sand grains are caught and left countless numbers of microscopic plants and animals that dwell at the surface of the sea. The fiddlers walk along the "windrows" as they are formed and with the spoon-shaped tips of their smaller claws or hands scoop up the food-laden sand and stuff it into their mouths as fast as their hands will work. At meal times the females have an advantage. Both of their hands have spoon fingers and both are kept busy. The crabs seldom enter the water, although their station so close to the water's edge exposes them to many a ducking in the wavelets. At times, too, when an enemy approaches from the land side the fiddler may elect to hide in the water, partially burying himself in the loose sand, rather than run for the burrow. These short intervals in the water are the most hazardous periods in the lives of adult fiddlers. Blue crabs like to lie in the shallow water and wait for little fish that get stranded, and they have learned that they can also pick up a considerable number of fiddlers. When the tide begins to rise and no new "windrows" are left on the beach the fiddlers will wander elsewhere in search of food. They will climb about over stones or pilings at the water's edge and always there are a few that lose their footing in spite of their eight legs and fall overboard. A fiddler overboard is a fiddler lost. They cannot swim, and hungry fishes, like the black sea bass and the sheepshead, quickly gobble them down.

As with the fiddler, so with other crabs and decapods with variations to best meet the exigencies of their existence. The length of time required for a typical decapod to grow from a magalops larva to maturity seems to be 208 days. A blue crab observed during this period molted fifteen times and grew from a width of a twenty-fifth of an inch to seven inches. The usual term of life for the blue crab seems to be about three years. J. Pearson deduced that the English crab, *Cancer pagu-*

rus, keeps on growing for some twelve years. There is reason to believe that after the fifth year the male molts only once in two years and the female once in three. Judging from the growths of shell and barnacles on old specimens, molting may cease completely as age advances. Incidentally, there is a fine series of cast shells made up of fifteen shells cast by an English shore crab, *Carcinus maenas,* over a period of three years. The crab molted seventeen times, and all its cast shells are shown in the accompanying photograph (Fig. 48) except two which were accidentally destroyed.

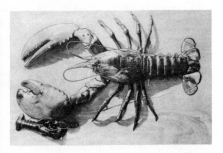

FIG. 48. Series of cast crab shells. Collected from one individual of the English shore crab (*Carcinus maenas*) (x 1/6). Courtesy of the British Museum.

FIG. 49. Giant American lobster (*Homarus americanus*) compared with an ordinary specimen. This giant measured twenty-four inches in body length and weighed twenty-eight pounds. Courtesy of Whipple Brothers, Matunuc Beach, Rhode Island.

We do not know which of the crustaceans is the longest-lived, but it may well be that the full-grown Northern lobster (Fig. 49) deserves this title of distinction. Thirty-five pounds was until recently the record weight and one of that size was estimated to be about fifty years of age. A few years ago a 44½-pound one was caught a hundred twenty five miles off the coast of

FIG. 50. The giant crab of Tasmania, *Pseudocarcinus gigas*, which attains a body width of as much as eighteen inches. Courtesy of Herbert M. Hale and the South Australian Museum.

Long Island. Such lobsters measure two feet in length of body alone. Their large crushing claws may well run to a length of twenty inches and an equal girth; that is, they are as big around as a man's head.

The really gigantic Crustacea are the fearsome-looking giant spider crabs of Japan and Northern Pacific waters, *Macrocheira kaempferi* (Fig. 5), which spans twelve feet from tip to tip of outstretched arms and measures eighteen inches across the body, while the huge Tasmanian *Pseudocarcinus gigas* (Fig. 50) attains a width sixteen inches, weighs as much as thirty pounds, and has a pincer as much as seventeen inches long from base of hand to tip of movable finger.

The largest fresh-water crayfish is also Tasmanian—a species that is all of two feet in length and weighs eight to nine pounds. Excellent eating, it is much sought after, but the small streams which it frequents seem an incongruous habitat for so large a crustacean.

Within the borders of the United States we have a giant fresh-water shrimp, *Macrobrachium carcinus*. The largest specimen I have seen weighed three pounds; its body length was ten and a half inches; the feelers, which were missing, were said to have been twenty-six and a half inches long; the larger cheliped of its sturdy pair, measured thirteen and a quarter inches. It hailed from the Devil's River, Texas.

The young of many fresh water decapods hatch out substantially in the form of the adult. One can readily see the advantage of this to species that may live in steep mountain torrents debouching into the sea, where it is but a hop-skip-and-jump from fresh to salt water; for if the young hatched out in a helpless larval stage they could not escape being washed into the sea, in which they would perish as the result of the salinity, just as we would be overcome by drinking highly concentrated salt solutions.

But among marine species such a suppression of the usually numerous larval transformations is of great rarity. Of the thousands of species of marine crabs, in only three is there definite evidence of a complete suppression of the larval stages such as we know in fresh-water forms.

The first case of direct development in marine crabs was discovered by Dr. Mary J. Rathbun, Associate in Zoology of the Smithsonian Institution. She found in the brood pouch of a small spider crab—*Naxioides serpulifera,* from the Monte Bello Islands (off the northwest coast of Australia)—young crabs in adult form; and not only in one stage, but in two, showing that at least one molt was undergone while the offspring were still under maternal care. It is of more than passing interest that the other two known instances of direct development in marine crabs should likewise have been found in Australian waters; both were dromiid sponge-carrying crabs—*Petalomera lateralis* and *Cryptodromia octodentata.*

The philosopher might find food for reflection in the fact that one of the best known of all crustaceans is a

thief, as the coconut crab of the South Seas, *Birgus latro*
has been called. *Birgus* is said to climb the coconut
palm to cut down the meaty nuts for food, although
whether it actually does the cutting down is still open
to question—for the habits and the life history of this
crab have not yet been investigated with any degree of
completeness. The robber crab is an agile and ready
climber, be it on coral blocks, volcanic cliffs, door jambs,
or trees.

Two friends who have had these crabs as pets in their
native islands have told me their sharp-pointed feet
found footholds in the crevice between the door jamb
and the wall, permitting them to climb up with ease; on
occasion they traveled sloth-like, though not so slowly,
along a wire stretched across the room. In descending,
use was made of window frames as well as door jambs. I
am not satisfied with Dr. P. F. Kopstein's claim that
falling with folded legs is the crab's usual mode of
descent from palm trees, despite his qualification that
under these circumstances the crab must restrict its
activities to low trees or get wrecked on the stones and
coral blocks commonly found in coconut groves. If this
is right we must credit the robber crab with ability to
single out low palms from high ones and to determine
whether the ground beneath is soft enough to permit a
safe drop.

The alleged native method of catching these crabs
throws light on their mode of descent. The story is that
when a native locates one of these big crabs up a palm
tree, he climbs part way up himself and fastens a girdle
of grass around the tree. Then he retreats. The crab, in
turn, crawls backward down the trunk, feeling behind as
it descends. When the girdle of grass is felt or touched
the crab releases its hold on the tree, under the impression that it has reached the ground. The unfortunate
Birgus tumbles heavily to the earth, either stunned or
killed. Two Dutch officials in the New Guinea area told

Dr. L. B. Holthuis, carcinologist at the Leiden Museum, of this way of capturing robber crabs, and one reported that he had witnessed a similar procedure in the Celebes where stones were placed around the foot of the tree to insure the crab getting "smashed."

The habits of these high-climbing animals do differ in different localities, a fact which accounts for the wide divergence in the accounts about them. Dr. Edward H. Held, Research Professor in Radiation Biology at the University of Washington, who has spent some time in the South Pacific and paid quite a bit of attention to *Birgus* has written me that he has only read of the above, native method of capture, and that it is evidently not used in the Marshalls or Carolines, where he visited. He has seen crabs descending the *Pandanus* and *Morinda* trees anterior end foremost. He adds, however, it's "only on rare occasions that this has been observed and I do not doubt that they may sometimes back down. . . . The idea that *Birgus* deliberately falls from high trees seems completely impossible to me. . . . I had the good fortune at one time to observe several crabs feeding in a *Pandanus* tree off and on over a period of several hours and the crabs invariably climbed down."

Corroborative evidence on the climbing propensities of the robber crab has also been passed on to me by Dr. A. J. Bruce from the Fisheries Research Station in Hong Kong. For some time he had a pet *Birgus*, of which he wrote: "I found it very ready to climb coconut palms and quite difficult to remove once it had started up. It usually climbed the shady side of the trunk, regardless of the tree's inclination. . . . On the ground it appeared to walk in no special direction when in the full sun. However, when its path crossed the shadow of a palm trunk it would turn south and walk along the shadow until it reached the trunk and then start to climb."

This predilection for shade would seem to be quite in keeping with the reactions of an animal of generally nocturnal habits. Some researchers feel that it is because of this, and to be out of the way of rats during sleep, that robber crabs climb trees.

In some districts it would appear that the robber crab makes his home some distance from the sea, on stony plateaus thirty or forty yards above the shore line. In the Solomon Islands, specimens have been seen at an elevation of three hundred feet. It is here, too, that the robber crab ejects large burrowing land crabs from their homes and takes over their underground habitations. Generally in the South Seas the robber crab seems to stay very close to shore, where it hides among the coral blocks and crevices of the reef, and, more rarely, under the roots of mangroves.

Baiting is an approved method of capturing the robber crab, but hunting him is more popular. On some of the South Pacific islands it is a sport attended with considerable excitement, because of the animal's wary habits, great strength, and bulldog tenacity. The chase usually is conducted at night, when the robber crab ventures from its daytime hiding places to feed. Improvised torches and lamps furnish the necessary light. When hunting over the reefs in the dark, the well-shod foreigner is at a decided disadvantage compared to the barefooted native, who can stalk the wary game noiselessly. The crab usually scuttles off with awkward yet effective backward rushes, covering several yards with each rush. It never turns tail to the danger. The claws are held presented for instant action, pincers pointing downward, in a posture like that assumed for guarding the head and face in sword exercise, but with the added advantage that it serves to guard not only the crab's head and eyes but its "solar plexus"—the abdomen—as well, for this poorly armored abdomen is its most vulnerable point. Then, too, the crab holds one or both of the needle-sharp second legs poised for a dangerous downward thrust. Altogether *Birgus* is a most doughty combatant when fully on guard, and one that seems to have no enemies to tear except man, although pigs which have run wild are said to attack and destroy the "robber." No doubt if one or a few pigs only attacked one of these powerful crabs the crab would be more than a match for the enemy. But wild pigs have a habit of running in droves, and in a combat with such a drove the odds would be heavily against the *Birgus*.

When surprised by torchlight the robber crab must be grasped with celerity by the carapace and held at arm's length until he can otherwise be secured. Woe betide the unskilled hunter who should get caught in its fearsome nippers; for the crab will amputate a finger quicker than it takes to tell about it. Fortunately, should it gain a hold with its claws, there is a little trick that results in instant release, and that is to give the tenacious fellow a rap on the abdomen. Otherwise, *Birgus* seems able to retain its grip for hours at a time.

Professor E. Wolf once had occasion to test the endurance of one of these suspended coconut crabs, which had happened to seize the handle of his insect-collecting net. As he couldn't wrench the net out of the animal's grasp, he placed enough stones in it to weigh five and a half pounds. For one full hour the crab showed no sign of fatigue, and it was some hours later before it finally let go its hold.

Some robber crabs grow to eighteen inches in length and no doubt have claws as large and strong in proportion. No other known animal has strength and ability to open the tough-husked coconut unaided. To get at the meat of the coconut, the robber crab drills out the eye of the nut—either green or ripe. But it is believed the crab can also crack the nut, as well as strip off the outer husk. When a hole is made, the crab uses one of its smaller legs to scrape out bits of the meat.

I have heard that robber crabs from regions where coconuts are to be had will starve rather than take other food; though where cocoa palms are lacking, as on Christmas Island, they seem willing to eat the fruits of other plants, such as the sago palm and screw pines. A robber crab can stow away about two coconuts each three days. It can readily be seen that it must be reckoned with where coconuts are grown for profit. But the rich diet renders the crab such a fat and juicy morsel himself that he is considered an epicurean treat by the non-Muhammadan natives, and so a destructive pest becomes a marketable product. One crab's abdomen will yield as much as a quart of oil. The Chinese, especially, value this crab's flesh as a delicacy; and in the regions where robber crabs abound, these people frequently keep them tethered about their dwellings—after depriving them of their powerful claws—to fatten them for the table. The orthodox Muhammadans, on the other hand, it is said, are twice interdicted by their religion from partaking of this delectable dish: first, because the animal uses its hand to convey its food to its mouth; and second, because it leads a double life, being a marine animal that passes its life upon the land.

The robber crab does go down to the sea, however, when its eggs are about to hatch, so that its young may be rocked in the cradle of the deep, the ancestral home of all Crustacea. The first free larva is a very ordinary form, like the usual hermit-crab zoea.

As a result of being so assiduously hunted on economic as well as gastronomic grounds, the robber crab seems to be rapidly disappearing, and in fact has been exterminated on many islands where it formerly abounded.

Some decapods play as important a role in the life of the baleen whales as do the copepods, amphipods, and euphausiids. These are the flattened shrimp-like forms known as galatheids, which occur in all major seas at times in incredible swarms. Were it not so the whales would not be able to gulp them down by the barrelfull, or by the ton perhaps, for the average galatheid measures, from rostral tip to end of telson, about an inch and a half in length. Carrying their chelipeds, or claws extended forward, in posture they are not too remotely reminiscent of juvenile lobsters. Whalers must so have felt about them, for they call these galatheids "lobster krill."

The "lobster krill" with which we are most familiar, *Pleuroncodes planipes*, in season occurs in great swarms off the coast of Lower California at, or within a fathom or two of the surface. It occurs also off the Mexican coast south of the peninsula.

Some conjectures regarding the abundance of these crustaceans were ventured by a Russian exploratory fishing expedition which operated for a time in an area of between seventy-five and eighty thousand square miles off the Lower California coast in 1959. Granting that there was a "crab" to each square yard of that great area, the Soviet biologist believed that some two hundred billion *Pleuroncodes* must have been present, drifting or swimming about at the time. He estimated that the total mass of galatheids in the area totaled three hundred thousand tons, all good whale food.

Happening on dense masses or separate aggregations of lobster krill the California gray whales enjoy feasts when they resort, at calving time, to the sunny lagoons on the ocean side of the peninsula. As the North Pacific whales travel to their nurseries in Mexican latitudes during northern winters, so the baleen whales from "down under" and the Antarctic seas during their southern winters go to bear their young and feed upon the *Pleuroncodes* species found in Peruvian and Ecuadorian latitudes.

Swarms of these reddish, or as some describe them, orange crustaceans tend to color the sea for great distances. Twice in recorded history this Lower California species of lobster krill was blown in to form windrows on shore in Monterey Bay, five to six hundred miles north of its normal tropic range. The first of these unusual occasions was reported by William Stimpson, one of the leading American authorities on Crustacea in his day: "This species lives in the open ocean and is sometimes found in vast quantities in the Pacific Ocean off the American coast. . . . In March, 1859, it was thrown ashore in considerable numbers at Monterey Bay, California. . . ." Though some *Pleuroncodes* had been casually noted at sea in 1948 and three or four times in the Bay in the '50's, one hundred and one years elapsed before another mass stranding was observed: January 12, 1960. This, Peter W. Glynn, then with the Hopkins Marine Station, reported as forming a band two yards wide and three hundred feet long. Remarking upon it, he said, "Despite considerable gorging by shore birds, and collecting by enthusiastic fishermen, an estimated ten thousand individuals were left in this band. With a minimum estimate of five thousand cast ashore the next day, the grand total beached, before predation and collecting by the public, probably was close to thirty or forty thousand." Over and above the "red crabs" on the beach, great numbers must have been milling about in the waters off shore. Just two weeks and a day later (January 27) the Station vessel ran through a sizeable "shoal" of these crustaceans upon which gulls, cormorants, and other sea birds were levying a heavy toll.

This unusual straying far from their tropic home was occasioned by exceptionally rare shifts of warmer waters northward, permitting these crustaceans and other southern forms of marine life to move into areas which for them are ordinarily occupied by inhospitably cold waters.

Studies carried out by the Scripps Institution, and the Inter-America Tropical Tuna Commission have indicated that *Pleuroncodes* also forms an important part of the food of the albacore, and the yellow fin and skipjack tunas—particularly the yellow fin.

Though we have been emphasizing the lobster krill of

the Lower California waters, the importance of crustaceans of all kinds along the West coast as food for these economically valuable fish should not be overlooked. In the stomachs of 2,846 yellow fin tunas from the Eastern Tropical Pacific, Crustacea accounted for almost forty-six percent of the stomach contents. Included were representatives of seven orders, sixteen families. For one thousand and ten skipjacks the count is much the same: six orders, twelve families; the percentage of crustacean remains in the stomach contents though was considerably higher, a shade over fifty-nine percent.

My own first experience with *Pleuroncodes* was near midnight, July 19, 1938, while steaming along south of Cape St. Lucas aboard the U.S.S. "Houston" with Galapagos-bound President Roosevelt, when Lt. H. K. Gates, one of the engineer officers, called me to the engine room. The suction side of one of the ship's condensors which had been opened up to ascertain why it had ceased to function, was found jammed with a mass of bright red galatheid shrimp—the familiar Lower California *Pleuroncodes planipes.*

With this we conclude our survey of the world of Crustacea. To compress so vast an assemblage into so small a space would be beyond the skill of man, but at least we have, metaphorically speaking, shaken hands with representative citizens of the subclasses. Further acquaintance with some of the idiosyncrasies may make it easier for us to recognize and better appreciate them.

IV. Crustacean Habits and Homes

Where we least expect them is often where we encounter Crustacea. The extremes of temperature under
which they may carry on the business of life are as-
tounding. Our common fresh-water amphipod, *Gammarus limnaeus*, which is active under six to seven feet of
ice on the Arctic coast of North America, occurs also in
the water flowing from boiling springs in the Yellow-
stone National Park. The temperature in which it thrives
there is nearly 100° F. The unicellular Protozoa, most
resistant of animals to heat, live in Italian hot springs
where the temperature reaches 130° F.; the nearest
approach to this achievement by another animal is made
by an ostracod that is abundant in certain Algerian
thermal waters, where the temperature ranges from 113°
to 123° F. The peracaridan *Thermosbaena* lives at 112°.

The water a mile or more below the surface of any
sea is exceedingly cold and, barring local differences,
uniformly so. The calculated mean temperature below
two thousand fathoms—more than two miles—is something like 35° F., and bottom ooze brought from that
depth, even at the equator, feels as cold to the touch as

melting ice. The fact that all the ocean abysses are chilled explains why the same species of animal may be found at opposite ends of the earth, and may pass quite comfortably beneath tropic seas, where surface temperatures are over 80° F.

There was a time when bringing up an animal from the depths of the sea was quite an achievement, and for that reason *Eurythenes gryllus*, a large amphipod which lives approximately three and three quarter miles down, on the bottom of the sea from Cape Horn to Greenland, long held the record for depth. But oceanographic facilities have improved in the last generation or so, and today *Macrostylis galatheae*, an isopod, holds the record. It was taken from six miles down, on the bottom or perhaps the sides of the trench lying east of the Philippines.

A specimen of the shrimp *Benthesicymus moratus* taken by the Prince of Monaco from a depth of three and a half miles, was "soft and lacking the carapace and most of its thoracic appendages." It is a well-known fact that animals brought up from great depths often reach the surface in a most wretched condition—soft and flabby, and, if they are fishes, turned inside out. This is to be expected considering the pressure to which they are subjected in their normal environment—something like four tons to the square inch.

Going toward the other extreme of the vertical scale, we find that amphipods and isopods have been collected in the Ecuadorean Andes at an elevation of 13,300 feet. At an elevation just eight hundred feet lower than this, in the Peruvian Andes, lies Lake Titicaca, that mighty body of fresh water 138 miles long and nearly seventy miles across at its widest point. Here, Alexander Agassiz in 1875 dredged nine species of Crustacea, of which seven were then new to science.

Many groups of Crustacea are represented in the underground faunas of the world. Blind crayfishes have long been known from our more famous caves, and amphipods, isopods, and copepods are to be numbered among the residents of such places.

Trees have their crustaceans. Best known is the widely distributed tree-climbing crab, *Aratus pisonii,* the mangrove crab so common in the mangrove swamps of the Americas, from Florida south. As with any other good crab its young are spawned in the salt or brackish water. Also called the tree crab because of its habits, it is well adapted to its mode of life, feeding to some extent at least on the leaves of the mangrove.

Then there are the crabs which resort to the larger bromelia water pockets or "tanks" as they are commonly referred to, to hatch their eggs. The megalops stages of these fairly small, about three-quarters inch wide, more or less arboreal, tree-climbing crabs, *Metapaulias depressus,* are fairly common in the uplands of Jamaica, where, with very rare exceptions they are found between the thousand foot and the three thousand foot levels.

In pockets of water at the bases of the leaves of the tropical bromeliads we find a species of ostracod found nowhere else. Copepods are known from the reservoirs of pitcher plants. Crustacea are as ubiquitous as mosquitoes, breeding in the merest bit of water that may persist long enough for the performance of a hasty life cycle.

Since Fritz Müller first discovered the ostracod *Metacypris bromeliarum* in the auxuliary catch basins of the Brazilian bromeliads, the search for crustaceans in queer places has produced remarkable results. Tropical palms and similar plants affording more or less permanent reservoirs of water, however tiny, pitcher plants of all kinds, damp and sodden moss hollows, and knot holes in trees have been examined. None of these has failed sooner or later to yield some form of crustacean life.

Crustaceans are even to be met "flying" through the air. We have long known that several pelagic copepods are energetic jumpers. In proportion to their size, their leap into the air is literally a modest flight, and has been described as such for *Pontellina mediterranea*. Individuals of this species have been observed launching themselves into the air by a powerful jump and then describing a long curve before falling back into the water. Their flight is thought to be comparable to that of the flying squirrel and flying fish, rather than to the hop of wingless crickets, for these creatures are well furnished with "feathered" appendages which, airplane-wise, lengthen out the curve of their fall.

Of the remarkable travels of crustaceans, none perhaps surpasses that of the mitten crab of the Orient, *Eriocheir sinensis*. *Eriocheir* means "woolly handed" and refers to the furry cuff of long hair enveloping each claw. In China the superstitious hold it to be the evil cause of the intermittent rat-and-mouse plagues that overrun the ripening fields of rice; they believe the rodents to be but four-legged transformations of the mitten crab. Even as early as the fourth century Yu Pau wrote: "In the year 283 A.D., all crabs in the District of Hwui-Ki were turned into rats, whose kind covered the rice farms and caused widespread destruction and devastation. When yet immature, these rats had hair and flesh but no bones, and were unable to pass over the dykes on the farms, but became vigorous after a few days." Though found at all times in the brackish water of estuaries, the mitten crab is first and foremost a fresh-water species, ranging up the Yangtse-kiang more than eight hundred miles from the sea.

In 1923 a specimen of this crab was brought to the Hamburg Museum for identification. It had been found off the mouth of the Elbe River, roughly eight thousand miles from China. It is believed this species came to Germany soon after the turn of the century, in some steamer's ballast tanks. These crab immigrants thrived in German waters and were soon seen by the hundreds clinging to the underpinning of wharves. Today, they spread along the European coast from the Seine in

France almost to the head of the Gulf of Bothnia between Sweden and Finland.

Eriocheir must spawn in salt water, but much of its adult life of at least a year is spent in fresh-water rivers. Tremendous hordes travel miles upstream in European rivers, as in Chinese water courses. Since, in Europe, marketing them has not been a success, the problem of what to do with these myriads of crabs is a considerable one.

Our familiar east coast blue crab, *Callinectes sapidus,* has also traveled far from home. In the early 1950's it had made its way to Holland and Denmark from southwest France, and in the last few years, all the way to the Mediterranean shores of Israel.

Another, earlier European visitant was *Rithropanopeus harrisii,* our common east coat mud crab which reached Holland incognito before 1874, not having been correctly identified; today it is also plentiful in South Harbor, Copenhagen, and most recently it has been reported from the Caspian sea. *Rithropanopeus* long ago turned up on our own West Coast whence it must have traveled overland with shipments of seed oysters. Dr. Torben Wolff, who checked on crustacean travels, does not believe these species crossed the ocean by clinging to ships' sides or living in growths of algae on the hulls, for the blue crab never occurs on piles; moreover, *Rithropanopeus* is a brackish water species unused to high salinities. He finds it more likely that these two species, like the *Eriocheir,* traveled in the ballast tanks of ships.

In 1963 a common Oriental shrimp *Palaemon macrodactylus* was found in San Francisco Bay. The *Palaemon* too must have traveled in the ballast tanks or salt water cooling system of some vessel, perhaps the same one that carried the barnacle *Balanus amphitrite hawaiiensis,* which is now found east and west, around the world. Another barnacle, the Australian *Elminius modestus,* no longer as modest as its name indicates, has also acquired the wanderlust. It spread first to England, then France and the low countries, and most recently to Germany; however, its northward spread may be limited by low temperatures.

Vessel transport, too, brought the amphipod *Amphithoe penicillata* from Pondichery, India, to the harbor of Marseilles; and at another time it brought a large West African swimming crab to the same harbor. The bottoms of ships have long been known as prime movers in the dispersal of certain forms of marine life through the oceans. The old days of wooden ships account for the universal distribution of that noted destroyer of wood, the isopod, *Limnoria lignorum,* and his boon companion, the amphipod, *Chelura terebrans.*

On South Atlantic hydrographic charts are often indicated "islands" of kelp which drift from the southern part of South America eastward past Falkland Islands. These are natural rafts, some of which, I should judge, would carry anything short of an elephant; certainly they carry many crustaceans, and we find the Falklands peopled with species common to South America.

The natural distribution of Crustacea holds the clue to a number of problems of zoogeography. I once picked up from the beach on the island of Juan Fernandez (off the coast of Chile) a grapsoid crab hitherto only recorded from New Zealand; and some time previously Professor Chilton had reported, also from South America, the occurrence of a New Zealand amphipod. Such natural history linkages are significant indexes of what may have been the distribution of the land masses of the earth in past geological ages. The truly wonderful flora of Juan Fernandez goes back to Tertiary times, geologically speaking—twenty-five million years ago or thereabouts. It would seem that the genealogy of the New Zealand shore crab, found on the same island, may perhaps be traced back to as remote a past to account for its presence on the island that was once the home of the prototype of Robinson Crusoe—Alexander Selkirk.

Cabo dos Camaraõs and Rio dos Camaraõs were the names given by the venturesome Portuguese navigators of the fourteenth century to the well-known West African promontory and bay that bear these names today. The "Cape of Shrimps" and "River of Shrimps" were so named because of the periodic nuptial swarming in this river of an obscure species of marine crustacean. In but slightly altered form, the Portuguese designations were later adopted by the various seafaring nations and inscribed upon their charts from the earliest times. Not only did the name come in time to embrace the neighboring coast, but the hinterland as well; and Kamerun became the official name for the former German colony, of which the French and British version is Cameroon.

The crustacean in question is the little shrimplike estuarine burrower, *Callianassa turnerana*. When this species swarms the number of individuals that rise to the surface of the water and swim about is literally incalculable. This prodigious swarming takes place in August, at approximately three-year intervals, and endures from three hours to a week or ten days, during which time all work is suspended by the native tribes in the region and a grand fête declared for the fishing and eating of this delicacy. During the swarming great stretches of the estuaries turn white with the pale-colored crustaceans. They suggest the silver horde of Pacific salmon running upstream on the inevitably fatal spawning journey. The *mbeatoe*, as the natives call the shrimp, disappears as abruptly as it came.

To catch *Callianassa*, the men wade out waist deep into the water with baskets and canoes. Every dip of the basket in the water means a full take of shrimp. The fishery appears to be prosecuted only in the evening and at night, and, failing moonlight, each of the many boats is provided with its flaming fagot.

During the swarming period the natives consume such

vast quantities of crustaceans that great piles of the discarded carapaces accumulate in all directions, and, rotting under the tropic sun, produce a most awful stench. One wonders whether after all it was not the smell rather than the swarming of the shrimp that lingered longest in the memories of the Portugese navigators who gave the place its name.

Crustacean homes are as interesting, and as varied, as their travels. The crab and such of his relatives as are bottom- or shore- or land-dwelling types are householders, each after his own manner. Some of these fellows are builders and display marvelous ingenuity in fashioning, with their claws and legs, the often recalcitrant materials of their environment into homes. Others are lazier but no less shrewd, for they preempt mollusks' shells or other suitable retreats and thus acquire their homes at no cost to themselves.

This record takes no account, of course, of the endless variety of Crustacea that swim or are wafted about in the water for the length of their days. For them the word home is meaningless.

The simplest type of shelter among crustaceans is, perhaps, that made use of by the edible crabs of our coasts, which bury themselves in the sand or mud either for protection or to conceal themselves in order to surprise their prey. On weedy or rocky shores, many crustaceans will hide among seaweeds or rocks. The number that seek shelter in other living animals or in imperishable animal remains is legion. Hermit crabs are found in mollusk shells the world over. Tiny shrimps, like the pontoniids and synalpheids, reside within the canals of sponges, making of them veritable marine apartment houses (Fig. 51). Other forms nestle down on coral polyps, allowing the latter to grow up around them to form a nest. Often, as the growth of their host continues, they find themselves unable to escape and so become emprisoned for life. Still others live in worm tubes

FIG. 51. Shrimps (*Synalpheus brooksi*) living in the canals of the loggerhead sponge. Photograph by A. S. Pearse.

FIG. 52. Slime-lined burrow of the sipunculid worm *Urechis*. The worm (left) catches food particles in a funnel of mucus. The food is plundered by both the crab (*Scleroplax*) and the small worm (left corner). Fishes are seeking shelter. After Fisher and McGinitie.

of various descriptions. The California sipunculid worm *Urechis,* like the parchment worm of our east coast (which builds a U-shaped tubular dwelling), gives shelter to certain crabs, to say nothing of other animals (Fig. 52). All the lodgers partake of the food particles carried into the tubular housing by the currents set up therein by the worm. As in so many partnerships of this kind, direct benefit to the host still remains to be demonstrated; but for the commensals the advantages of the association are many and obvious, and not the least of them is the prolonging of the breeding season in these species of crabs.

Edible mollusks in all parts of the world are infested by commensal crabs. At Hampton Roads, the headquarters of the Chesapeake Bay oyster industry, it is possible to get females of the little oyster crab in great quantities; the male is less often seen. The female, sheltered and sedentary, has become quite soft of shell and appears rather helpless when removed from its abode, which under ordinary circumstances it seems never voluntarily to forsake. Not so with the male, which visits about from shell to shell, calling on the ladies. It is, moreover, hard of body and rounded, so that an occasional nip resulting from the unanticipated closing of a mollusk shell will tend to squeeze it in or out with no more harm than the loss of a limb or two—a trifling matter in the life of a crustacean.

Copepods and crabs are not the only crustacean commensals; a host of shrimps have also adopted this style of living. But although it is rare to find more than one crab in a shell—and that one always the female—the two sexes in many species of shrimps are quite inseparable.

But the crustacean home-making we have been describing is like renting a furnished apartment with hotel service. The situation is quite otherwise with the crustacean builders. Land crabs are energetic excavators wherever they occur. Fiddler crabs especially are well known

for their digging propensities, and they usually spend
each high tide safely immured in a retreat constructed
for the purpose and furnished with a bubble of air for
respiration. The fiddler is enough of a builder to give the
ground upon which he plans to make his home a preliminary testing out with his feet. If it has the right feel he
begins operations. As he digs he scrapes out the sand,
rolls it into pellets, cradles it in some of his feet, and
deposits it at the mouth of the hole or burrow—unless
this interferes with the work, in which case he moves it
away.

The depth of the burrows is remarkably uniform in a
given area and has been found to be conditioned by the
depth to which the moisture penetrates the sand. The
crab often plugs the entrance with a "cork" of sand or
mud and sits safely ensconced within for as much as
several days at a time. Invariably as the tide rises he
closes the burrow tightly to imprison the air contained
in the end chamber.

Continued existence for most Crustacea is probably at
the price of eternal vigilance. The fiddlers and other
architects of beach homes will illustrate this vigilance.
Coming out of its burrow with a load of sand and pebbles, the fiddler stops at the circular front door and carefully surveys the surrounding terrain with stalked eyes,
which are articulated periscopes no less, to make sure
that the coast is clear before it ventures farther.

Like human artisans, the fiddlers must have their
"sport," it seems. The most amusing incident of this sort
concerns two male fiddlers of medium size that Doctor
A. S. Pearse once watched running about for perhaps half
an hour over an area twelve to fourteen yards in diameter. "They kept close together and acted like two mis-
chievous sailors ashore. The tide was coming in rapidly,
and in their rambles the pair came to a place where a
large slow-moving (crab) was carrying a plug to close
his burrow. They waited until the plug had been pulled

down over the owner, then (one of them) went to the hole and removed it; and as the outraged owner emerged the plug remover and his mate scuttled off toward the former's burrow."

Most naturalists believe that the waving of the large claw of the male is an amatory gesture to attract the female—to show the lady of his affections that he is a "crab among crabs." In a number of species the great chela is very beautifully colored, but whether the color as well as the motion exercises a potent influence on the sensory perceptions of the female has been questioned. Dr. J. Verwey has suggested that the claw is waved to warn off intruders from each crab's own particular eminent domain. Except for the fact that the waving of the large claw, in some species at least, seems to be restricted to certain times of the year, his point may be well taken, for did the various males not keep all other crabs at sufficient distance there would not be enough food or "grazing" ground about the mouth of each burrow to nourish the many individuals always found crowded together in every fiddler community.

Ocypode, the ghost crab, often digs a burrow as much as four feet deep in order to get down to moist sand, after which the burrow is continued in a more or less lateral direction as a tunnel. Fiddlers seldom go deeper than a foot. The *Ocypode* will sometimes have a second entrance or exit to its home, though it is seldom used as such. It has been suggested that this is for ventilation—a very intelligent provision, if true. After stocking the burrow with food, *Ocypode* has been observed to draw two loads of sand into the entrance, thus practically closing it, but leaving the distal joints of the walking legs outside. These carefully tamp down the plug and finally are quickly drawn in, leaving sometimes only a very small hole and sometimes none at all. By this means the entrance to the burrow is very effectually concealed.

Professor R. P. Cowles reported having seen crabs of this genus lying on their backs in their tunnels digging away at the roof, and he surmised that this is probably the manner in which a vertical passage is started.

It is difficult to leave the subject of burrowing crabs without a few words about the habits of the sand bubbler, *Scopimera inflata,* and of the little soldier crab, *Mictyris longicarpus,* of Australasia.

The sand bubblers occur in great numbers and make their presence known by millions of tiny pellets of sand on the beach. As the tide recedes they scramble to the surface and proceed to repair their burrows. Each one bores a clean cylindrical hole from three to fifteen inches deep, depending apparently on the depth of the looser and more watery sand below the surface (Fig. 53). This accomplished, the sand bubbler begins feeding.

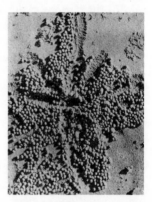

FIG. 53. A twelve-inch burrow with sand bubbler crab (*Scopimera inflata*) at the bottom. Courtesy of the Australian Museum.

FIG. 54. Pellets and trenches made by the sand bubbler crab when feeding. Courtesy of the Australian Museum.

In the words of F. A. McNeill, "he moves sideways from the mouth of his burrow and scoops out a narrow trench with his capable little nippers. The excavated sand is then passed into the lower portion of his capacious mouth-jaws, where it is carefully sieved for its contained

food-particles. It is then expelled from their upper portion and so manipulated as to form a rounded pellet.
Upon reaching a definite size, the pellet is passed backwards and deposited on the beach behind the crab,
which simultaneously moves on a pace outwards from its
burrow. In this way a feeding trench is formed, nine to
eighteen inches in length." (Fig. 54)

The soldier crab, so called because it maneuvers in
great armies over the sand flats at low tide, might just
as well be named the corkscrew crab, from its method
of digging in. The rapidity with which it sinks from
sight is almost magical. One may sometimes approach to
within six yards of these crabs, but an instant thereafter
an entire army will have vanished, in the manner illustrated in Figure 55. The soldier crab, which is about the
size of a large cherry, accomplishes this disappearance
by digging with the legs of one side and rotating at the
same time, so that the digging follows a spiral.

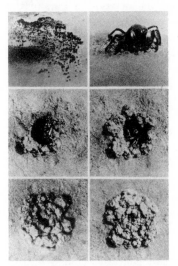

FIG. 55. How the soldier crab (*Myctris longicarpus*) digs in. Upper
left, an army of soldier crabs on the march. Courtesy of R. P.
Cowles.

The record for deep digging by any crustacean without question belongs to an American mound-building crayfish, *Cambarus diogenes*. Dr. Horton H. Hobbs, our American authority on these fresh water crustaceans, informs me that in the banks of the Apalachicola River, Florida, which is subjected to not infrequent high floods, he has noticed, and indeed excavated burrows made by this species that went a full twenty feet more or less vertically down into the high, steep mud banks of that river.

Burrow construction is common to many species of crabs and is met with in all parts of the world. It is this propensity that frequently makes crabs serious agricultural pests. But artisanship of this sort extends into other groups of Crustacea as well. Sand-fleas, beach hoppers, or scuds, dig with great celerity; nor do they cease activity when they get within the burrow, for there they busy themselves with their toilet. They are among the neatest of small animals, forever brushing and cleaning themselves. In some of them one or another pair of the appendages is especially slender and motile and so articulated as to reach in all directions and to all extremities, as though it were built expressly for the job of cleaning, properly and carefully, every portion of the creature's body. (Fig. 67, page 150, for similar activity in a shrimp.) These almost automatic brushes are at their busiest when the animal is otherwise at rest; and, since to do their work effectively they must themselves be kept clean, certain of the mouth appendages comb them from time to time, thus freeing them from the debris and grit they have accumulated.

In the Puget Sound region, the subterranean homes of the shrimp *Upogebia pugettensis* are certainly noteworthy structures. One such burrow found by Dr. Belle Stevens, of the University of Washington, descended to a depth of over a yard, spread laterally for a length of two feet, and had three different openings (Fig. 56. upper). The construction of such a dugout requires con-

FIG. 56. *Upogebia pugettensis* and its burrow. Upper, plaster cast of burrow with its occupant. Lower, dorsal view of a male. Courtesy of Belle Stevens.

siderable acrobatic ability. The tunnel system, at intervals of about six inches—roughly corresponding to the length of the grown animal from the tips of the extended claws to the end of the tail—has slight enlargements in which the curved animal reverses itself to carry out excavated material. The digging and the transportation of material to the surface are both done head-foremost, hence the need for turning end for end during the process.

A closely related South American shrimp constructs apartment houses in rock. The material is a soft shale, to be sure, but yet sufficiently hard to require considerable chipping and flaking with a geological hammer before the interior arrangements of the shrimp's house can be observed. I have seen one such house in three planes or stories, with "turn-abouts" such as Doctor Stevens described excavated in stone, but with this most remarkable difference—that no openings capable of permitting the exit of even a half-grown animal could be discovered. Apparently the shrimps begin their homes when young and add to them as they grow, but never attempt to forsake their stony dungeons.

Crustacea also make extensive use of wood in their building operations. The wood-boring isopods of cosmopolitan distribution (*Limnoria lignorum*) construct apartment houses in wooden harbor works to shelter their teeming millions (Fig. 57). Dr. F. A. McNeill of the Australian Museum found that they will live under what we would consider the worst kind of tenement conditions—three to four hundred individuals of all ages to the cubic inch, which represents considerable crowding even for an animal the adult of which is no more than a quarter of an inch in length.

FIG. 57. *Limnoria lignorum*, the wood-boring isopod, photographed in the act of burrowing (x 8). Courtesy of C. A. Kofoid.

In Charleston Harbor, South Carolina, unprotected piling lasts on the average only two years, due to the ravages of *Limnoria.* In Key West Harbor this species will destroy an unprotected pile in even less time. Nor does this crustacean respect creosoted timber. Professor C. A. Kofoid has described the situation: "It frequently gains entrance at a knot, abrasion, or other point of thin treatment, and works in until it reaches the untreated center of the stick. This portion of the timber is promptly destroyed and the outer treated shell left intact."

Professor Kofoid had the good fortune to observe *Limnoria* in action. He found that the body is so firmly held in position by the peculiar arrangement of the legs and clawlike feet that it is difficult to wash the isopod off the surface of the wood with a stream of water. In the boring process itself there is a very vigorous action of the mouth parts, especially of the mandibles and maxillipeds, combined with a slow turning of the head.

Usually associated with *Limnoria* is the wood-destroying amphipod *Chelura terebrans*. Because of its larger size the amphipod excavates slightly larger burrows, but the damage it causes is secondary to that occasioned by its isopod associate.

A number of isopods of the genus *Sphaeroma* are doughty carpenters and completely riddle large-diameter wood piling, pitch pine, and even palmetto in the course of their home building. Nor is stone construction—or destruction, if you prefer—neglected by these crustacean artisans. In San Francisco Bay extensive areas of San Pablo sandstone and Pinole tufa have been honeycombed by the isopod *Sphaeroma pentodon*; and so apt have these ordinarily marsh-inhabiting crustaceans become in working masonry that when brought into the laboratory aquariums they would tackle blocks of carpenter's chalk and bite out bits with their mandibles at a lively rate. In less than twenty-four hours one specimen had bored a hole in a chalk block deeper than its own length —a matter of a quarter of an inch or so.

In Hawkes Bay, New Zealand, *Sphaeroma quoyana* made such extensive use of a clay stone employed in harbor works that the sea wall in many places virtually disappeared, and blocks of concrete which overlaid the rock sank several feet. It is said that boring crustaceans are even making use of concrete structures for residential purposes. "If this be the case," Doctor W. T. Calman warned us, "it may become a matter of very grave concern for the engineer, in view of the increasing use of reinforced concrete for harbor works of all kinds . . . it would be well to avoid using rubble of calcareous or friable rock for mixing in concrete."

Limnoria has also been found exercising its boring propensities on submarine cables. In New Zealand it reportedly was the cause of a cable failure at a depth of sixty fathoms, having penetrated the rubber insulation at a splice to the extent of admitting the sea water to the inner core of the cable.

As remarkable as these excavations and borings are, we may feel them inferior to the handiwork of animals higher in the scale of life. We have all marveled at the skill displayed in the construction of the weaver bird's nest, but such avian tailoring is easily matched by the "needlework" of at least one crustacean. There is a shrimp, *Alpheus pachychirus,* that stitches tangles of seaweed together to construct branching tubes ten to twelve inches in length and three-fourths of an inch in diameter, usually with a somewhat larger chamber in one end. The alga used is fine and threadlike and grows in dense mats. The shrimp lies on his back in some convenient fold or furrow of these naturally interlaced mats and with his pair of slender chelate second legs pulls together the edges of the furrow (Fig. 58). He thrusts one of these legs through one edge of the mat like a needle and, catching a thread from the opposite edge, pulls it back through the first edge. Simple though this stitch is, it holds the mat edges firmly together.

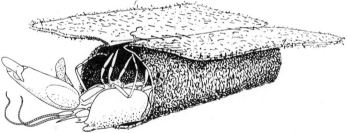

FIG. 58. *Alpheus pachychirus* stitching together the edges of a furrow in an algal mat to form a tubular retreat. After Cowles.

Moreover, our tailor is not to be outdone in cleverness by human seamstresses. He does not sew up the tube from end to end at once, but first stitches it together at intervals—bastes it—and then sews up the intervening places. So fast does this small artisan work that ten minutes suffice for him to form a tube four inches long.

With one exception each of the tubes that were examined by Professor Cowles contained two individuals, a male and a female.

FIG. 59. Four species of amphipod tube builders. Lower left, *Cymadusa*; upper, *Siphonectes*; central three, *Corophium*; right, *Ericthsonius*. (About x 3-4). After Della Valle.

Tube building among Crustacea is not confined to the shrimps. In the amphipods we find a number of almost equally surprising performances (Fig. 59). *Cerapus* builds a most serviceable tube, spun from a glandular secretion. Transparent when new, it soon becomes dark and opaque as the animal affixes to it by means of the sticky secretion tiny fragments of algae, hydroids, and the like, as well as a great many little pellets unidentifiable other than as the excrement of the animal. The tube is apparently never attached to its inhabitant, which, however, carries it about and is little more than an animated jack-in-the-box while under observation. The rapidity with which the amphipod's head appears first at one end of the tube and then at the other, especially when the animal is disturbed, is almost magical. To effect a change of location *Cerapus* apparently pulls himself and his housing over the ground.

A related amphipod, *Cyrtophium*, swims about in his tube, now in an upright position, now obliquely, now sinking to the bottom like an eddying morsel of driftwood. The tube is a bit of hollow grass stalk lined and overlaid with the hardened hyaline spinning-gland secretion. In repairing his dwelling *Cyrtophium* completely withdraws himself into its confines and then slowly but continuously keeps it revolving around himself. Where the tube is fixed, the animal must do the revolving to keep the tube in shape and condition.

Unciola, though tube-dwelling, is a lazy fellow, pre-empting the tubes of other amphipods or those constructed by worms. Some species of *Siphonectes* use an old *Dentalium* shell, the mouth of which they narrow to suitable proportions with agglutinated fragments of shell and pebbles. The hermit crab usually uses a shell as a dwelling (Fig. 60) without remodeling. However, the hinder body undergoes a series of anatomical modifications adapting it to the whorls of the shell becoming the crab's domicile (Fig. 61). The chelae adapt to fit the opening so as to form of them a door secure against the attacks of enemies.

FIG. 60. Hermit crabs (*Pagurus bernhardus*) at home in shells. After Schensky.

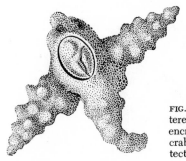

FIG. 61. Hermit crab sheltered in home formed by an encrusting bryozoan. The crab's big claw forms a protecting door.

A hermit will make use of some other protective shelter if there is no suitable mollusk at hand. Some members of the East Indian genus, *Coenobita,* have been seen with the abdomen stuck in the half of a coconut shell, in joints of bamboo, broken lamp chimneys, and other suitable substitutes. Crabs other than hermits have taken to molluscan protection, too; for example, *Hypoconcha.* Its back has become shaped so as to fit snugly into the half of a clam shell (Fig. 62). Such a home has no elasticity and, like that of the hermit, must be exchanged for a larger one from time to time as the inhabitant increases in size. *Dorippe,* "the crab with the human face" or the "demon-faced" crab (Fig. 63), has the same shell-carrying habit. In some parts of the Orient *Dorippe* is held sacred, for the slant-eyed face that is so readily to be traced in the areolations of his carapace is likened to the deceased relative whose soul has passed into the crab.

FIG. 62. *Hypoconcha* in a clam shell. Left, shell from above. Right, from underside. Center, dorsal view of crab showing hinder legs with which crab grasps the shell.

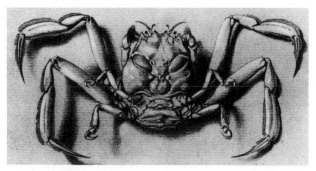

FIG. 63. *Dorippe,* called by the Chinese "the crab with the human face" because of the sculpture of its carapace.

Like *Hypoconcha,* other dromiid crabs have the hinder legs turned up over the back in order to support their protective housings. Houses of the dromiid crabs are indeed most wonderful affairs, increasing in size and in the protection they afford as the tenant grows. These unique and portable residences may be either live ascidians or sponges which the dromiid acquires in youth and totes about for life, unless it chooses to make a change. So well do these living bits of their environment conceal the dromiids that unless they are on the move they can be spotted only by the closest observer.

Under natural conditions a sponge-carrying dromiid in need of housing very methodically goes about cutting out the necessary material from a convenient sheet of incrusting sponge, using its chelae as a cutter. As the piece is freed somewhat and as soon as its edge can be raised, the crab gradually works himself under, cutting away till the whole piece is dislodged. Within a few days the growth of the sponge and also, no doubt, the trimming given it by the crab cause the rough edges of the cover to disappear and it takes on the regular shape of one that has been long in use for this purpose.

Where a sponge case is not as easily lifted as described above, the crab will trench the original groove more deeply, working after the manner of a man attempting to dislodge an object similarly attached. When the dromiid thinks the grooving and undercutting have gone far enough, it climbs above and, grasping the sponge with his claws at two points along the furrow, gives a good heave. If the sponge is too tightly seated, it goes back for another spell of undercutting.

Very often the case is too flat, and it never fits exactly to the surface of the crab's back. The crab corrects this by pressing the sponge tightly to its back and bending it out. As the tissues of the sponge are fairly plastic, it soon takes on a fairly definite shape, particularly as regards the inner concavity into which the crab's back fits. It has a definite cut and points of orientation of which the crab is fully cognizant, as the removal of its accustomed case will demonstrate. After its removal, if it is permitted to do so, the crab does not long delay in returning to its house. Taking hold of it with its chelae, the crab rolls over on its back, lifting up the case, concave side downwards, at the same time. Now the crab rotates the case with its legs; then, grasping it with the hooks of the fourth and fifth legs, it tilts its hinder margin into the air, at the same time sliding it down over its back as it stands on its head. This brings both case and crab into the proper position relative to each other, but for the moment both on their front ends—a position obviously of unstable equilibrium, which results in the crab falling on its feet in natural position or else on its back and in the case. Then the crab must needs right itself by any of the normal means known to crabs, with the case held meanwhile close to its back (Fig. 64).

If one tries to puzzle the *Dromia* by weighting the upturned case with small stones so that it is too heavy to be picked up by one of the usual modes, it will not be long before the animal has freed the case of the extraneous matter. Always the crab gives the case a preliminary try, and if the object proves too heavy, it presses its fore or hind part between the sponge and the ground until it overthrows the case and causes the stones to fall out.

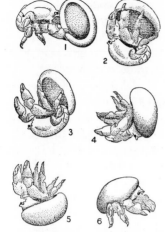

FIG. 64. The manner in which the dromiid crab (*Dromia*) puts on its sponge coat. After Dembowska.

Deprived of the materials provided by nature for fashioning the case, the dromiid will make use of paper or rags, if either of these is offered, or may even accept a man-made case of plastic clay. Usually the crab will quickly discard the paper or rags for a natural cover, but less readily the artificial clay case, especially if it has become accustomed to it for a period of time. In fashioning a paper case the dromiid is as clever with its claws as any child cutting out paper shapes with scissors. The crab usually begins working at one edge, from the underside of the paper, making little tears in it. Though these seem to be more or less irregular, the crab always works in a definite direction, taking hold, tearing, moving along, and tearing again, until an approximately elliptical piece is cut out. *Dromia* may work lying on its back beneath the paper or in its normal position, holding it with the other legs while the claws do the piercing and cutting. Rarely is the future case damaged in the making by a wrong or too great a tear.

Dromia gets so used to its own sponge case that it can usually pick it out from many other sponges. Among a variety of materials *Dromia* always seems to choose a sponge. When we try to puzzle this crab still more by hiding the case under pebbles, it will, if the performance has been gone over repeatedly and gradually, learn to look for it, even if completely concealed. If the case is anchored, *Dromia* is ingenious enough to effect its release. Miss W. S. Dembowska's account of experiments conducted to bring out these points had best be told in her own words:

> In another series of experiments I fastened the sponge to a little wire hook. In the meantime the crab manufactured a new case of paper. In order to make the sponge more conspicuous I chose a red one and put it into a porcelain dish, hanging it so high on the wall that the crab could hardly reach it. When I put the crab in, it directed itself at once toward the sponge, dropping the paper case on the way. With some difficulty the animal succeeded in grasping the hanging sponge with the chelae. It then climbed over the sponge, very soon found the wire hook, and began to tear off small pieces of sponge around it. After a short time the sponge became liberated and the *Dromia* rolled down with it, and put the sponge on the back. From the moment of putting the crab into the vessel to the liberation of the sponge, seven minutes elapsed.

Many spider crabs are make-up artists. Nature has kindly provided these decorator crabs with patches of hooked hairs on the back; and on these the crab impales seaweeds and other marine growths, after first chewing the lower ends to enable them to be more securely hooked to the crooked hairs (Fig. 65). Such decorated

FIG. 65. Decorator crab, *Eruma hispidum*. As found in nature and (left) cleaned of camouflage. Courtesy of the South Australian Museum.

crabs are verily traveling sea gardens. Sometimes sponges grow in such a garden, building up to most startling heights; and the crab could not transport them were it not for the supporting power of the water.

A well-masked crab is not only thoroughly concealed from all enemies, but also is most advantageously camouflaged for aggression. Crabs with these masking propensities exercise a fine sense of discrimination as to the fitness of their adornment. They have been subjected to numerous experiments designed to display their surprising faculty of dressing themselves like and with parts or bits of their surroundings. In an aquarium fitted with a choice of strips of colored paper, the crabs will always choose the pieces presenting or more nearly presenting the color of their surroundings. A long series of experiments seems to have proved that these crabs can distinguish colors and make advantageous use of their perceptions.

Monkeys in captivity have been known to use a stick to get something just out of reach, and some of the apes have employed a club. Certain wasps use a bit of rock in pounding down the mud plug of their tunnels; but it is less well known that Crustacea, too, among the lower animals, make use of tools or weapons which they take up and employ with intent and purpose. There are at least two such crustaceans—both crabs—which consciously travel about with accoutrements of which they make use on occasion. To be sure, the tools or weapons are living anemones, but they are intentionally and purposefully carried. *Lybia tessellata* (Fig. 66) and *Lybia leptochelis* are most unhappy without at least one anemone in one of their claws. The anemone seems always to be the same, *Triactis producta*. These are richly provided with nettle-cells and woe betide any small animal life coming in contact with them. The claws of *Lybia* are especially adapted for grasping the fleshy bodies of their involuntary weapons, and for holding them so as to prevent them from affixing themselves to

FIG. 66. A crab of the Indian Ocean, *Lybia tessellata*, bearing in its claws two sea anemones for defense. Adapted from Borradaile.

the crab's body by their basal discs. For want of anemone of suitable size, *Lybia* will even rend a fragment from one which may be carried in its other claw, or from another anemone too large to be carried. Usually the fragment survives as the anemone readily regenerates parts lost if at least a portion of its original oral-tentacular disc remains with the torn-off fragment.

No doubt *Lybia* in common with many other crustaceans is a bit of a scavenger, but if live small fish, amphipods, and the like are close by, the crab thrusts out its anemones. If contact is established the victim falls lifeless to the bottom where it is picked up by the second feet of the crab, which never willingly will lay down its weapons.

Well may we wonder what order of intelligence is this that can direct the being to which it pertains to take up an anemone and make use of its protective powers; even to distinguish between a useful one and a useless portion of one; to twist and turn the anemone about in the claws until satisfactorily fixed, shift its own position as necessary, and when danger threatens from any quarter, turn the batteries of nettle cells in that direction. Moreover, though at first warning the crab assumes the defensive, it does not foolishly trust everything to its weapons, but sensibly seeks flight usually among the interstices of the coral reef in which it makes its home, if the danger threatens to become overwhelming.

All this I have learned from Charles A. Cutress, a curatorial associate of mine in the National Museum, who has worked with and photographed these crabs in Hawaii. I am indebted to him also for further information about another crab, also found in Hawaii, which similarly employs anemones as a means of defense, *Polydectus cupulifer*. *Polydectus* is a most sluggish individual, more prone to hide away and play possum than to offer fight with its weapons. Yet the crab will defend itself when need to do so arises, says Cutress, although he has never observed *Polydectus* make use of his anemones for food gathering. This Indopacific crab usually carries the anemone *Telmatactis decora*, but unlike the more choosy *Lybia*, in some localities will carry other species and sometimes even small holothurians.

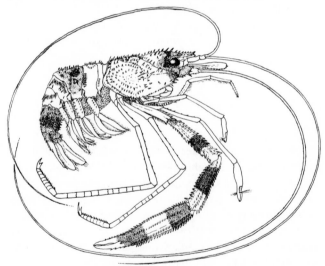

FIG. 67. *Stenopus hispidus*, the most conspicuously marked and perhaps the largest of the cleaner shrimp. It grows to a length of two and one half inches or better.

Before leaving our study of their habits, we should consider some crustaceans which provide a service to other dwellers of the deep. These are the so-called cleaner shrimps, including the boxer shrimp, *Stenopus hispidus* (Fig. 67), which remove parasites and extraneous debris from fishes. This crustacean behavior was discovered by Harry and Verne Pederson, brothers whose hobby was underwater photography. On a vacation in the Bahamas, they noticed fish congregating about some brightly-colored sea anemones among coral formations and close by, often standing among the tentacles of the anemones, small transparent shrimp, perhaps an inch and a half long. They have described and filmed the work of these shrimp. A number of fish gather around one, and one by one draw closer to it. When one is close enough, the shrimp moves out and climbs aboard, and moving rapidly over the fish, pulls and digs under attached parasites, dislodging and eating them if not too large. Wounds are given special attention, so that injured tatters or possibly loose tissue is removed. One side and then the other of these fish is overhauled. The finishing touch is climatic—the fish opens wide its gill covers and the shrimp enters the buccal cavity. The mouth of the fish opens and closes as it breathes, but the shrimp remains unharmed within until gills and the rest of this interior is overhauled and parasites are removed. When a shrimp appears to have finished it retreats to its anemone stand and unless satiated or tired takes on the next fish in line.

The cleaning of fish by other fish has long been known, but this cleaning by crustaceans was something quite new. The discovery excited considerable interest among marine biologists and led to further discoveries. Half a dozen species are now known. The one first discovered is named, appropriately, *Periclimenes pedersoni.*

V. Crustacean Conversation

Crustaceans are not the inarticulate beings we formerly took them to be. From such instances as we have of their ability to communicate with one another, it is entirely reasonable to believe that sound production in them is a widespread phenomenon. Certainly, they would have as many uses for sound production and perception as have other animals that hear and "speak."

Some Crustacea are very "garrulous" and make their presence known at the slightest provocation. One has only to walk over a coral reef where the "pistol crabs"—alpheid shrimps—abound at low tide to be bombarded from all sides by sharp reports. Of what use this noise is to its tiny makers is difficult to tell. Perhaps it is a warning signal from one animal to another, or possibly the little shrimp just can't help making it when snapping shut the larger and more powerful of its two claws. The pincers of these crustaceans are markedly dissimilar, and the larger, the "popgun" so to speak, is quite peculiarly built and usually appears very much distorted. The movable finger is provided with a little plug that fits snugly in a tubular pocket in the opposed fixed finger (Fig. 68,

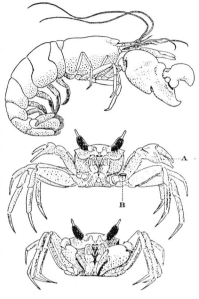

FIG. 68. "Speaking" crustaceans. Upper, pistol crab (*Alpheus pachychirus*) several times enlarged. Plunger and tubular socket can be seen in big claw. Middle, ghost crab (*Ocypode*) showing ridges on the big claw (A) which it rubs against the boss (B) when the claw is drawn in as in lower figure.

upper). The withdrawal of this stopper, like the sudden withdrawal of a tight-fitting cork, is said by many to be the cause of the sharp reports. But my own observations, as well as those of others, indicate rather that the sound is produced by the closing of the fingers one against the other. With such force do the two fingers come together that if a hard object, such as a piece of wire or a dissecting needle, be held in the open claw, one or the other finger is shattered by the force of the blow. One of these alpheid shrimps in a glass dish or small aquarium can make you think some one is giving the glass a smart blow with a tack hammer; and even though you know the cause, you cannot resist the feeling that each report spells the end of that particular piece of glassware.

Sounds of another kind are produced by our common East Coast mantis shrimp, the *Squilla empusa*. It makes a vigorous rasping noise by rubbing the uropods against the underside of the telson. This peculiar form of stridulating is also found in an Indian shrimp described by the late Colonel A. Alcock. In this shrimp the edge of the telson and the inner edge of each of the inner branches of the uropods "are finely burred like a rasp, so that when they are rubbed upon one another a soft trilling sound, like the subdued note of a grasshopper, results."

In such mechanisms as these, apparently designed specifically for sound-making, we have stronger indications than in the "popguns"—which may be purely accidental and incidental—that crustaceans actually communicate with each other.

The Florida spiny lobster also produces a good loud noise, comparable to that of a moist finger rubbed against a window pane. It does this by rubbing a specially developed flap on the antennules against the keeled orbital margin.

Dr. Mary J. Rathbun called attention to the fact that the heavy-bodied stone crabs of the genus *Menippe* are well provided with vocal organs, which vary according to the species (Fig. 69, below); and in the absence of

fig. 69. Stone crab (*Menippe mercenaria*). Note stridulating ridges on inner surface of the claws. Width of body in a large specimen exceeds five inches. After Mary J. Rathbun.

other criteria—at least in the American forms—each species may be distinguished by the vocal organs peculiar to it. These organs, in general, are variously organized patches of striae on the inner surfaces of the chelae that play against tubercles on the carapace. It is plausible that many of the stone crabs are more given to articulate utterance than has been suspected, a statement that can be borne out by observation of a relative of *Menippe* among the xanthid crabs—*Pseudozius bouvieri*. This fellow rubs the wrist, or carpal joint, of the cheliped against the edge of the carapace to generate a note akin to that produced by a grasshopper when it fiddles over its wing covers with the roughened thighs of its hind legs.

A simple row of tubercles or granules scraped by a ridge of no complexity might appear to be limited to the production of but one sound or tone, but Colonel Alcock discovered that the "ghost" crab, *Ocypode macrocera*, was capable of at least three tones. Although this species occurs in battalions, each individual has its own burrow, which it holds to be inviolable; and no other *Ocypode* ever voluntarily enters it. These crabs have to be on the constant lookout for attack by kites and jackals, and so it is essential for the continuance of the species that each individual should at all times have unimpeded access to its own home. As Colonel Alcock wrote:

> . . . if many crabs make a practice of crowding into one small burrow they would certainly run the risk of being suffocated, if not crushed to death outright. it seems probable, therefore, that it would be advantageous to the species as a whole if the rights of property in burrows were rigidly respected, and if each individual member possessed some means of giving notice that its burrow was occupied—or, as Mr. Stebbing has expressed it, that it was "not at home" to callers; and I think that this consideration

gives a clue to the use of the stridulating mechanism.

The sounds can be heard, and their effects seen, by forcing one crab, which we will call the intruder, into the burrow of another, which we will call the rightful owner. The intruder shows the strongest reluctance to enter, and will take all the risks of open flight rather than do so, and, when forced in, he keeps as near the mouth of the burrow as possible. When the rightful owner discovers the intruder, he utters a few broken tones of remonstrance, on hearing which the intruder, if permitted, will at once leave the burrow. If the intruder be prevented from making his escape, the low and broken tones of the rightful owner gradually rise in loudness and shrillness and frequency until they become a continuous low-pitched whirr, or high-pitched growl, the burrow acting as a resonator.

Apparently *Ocypode macrocera* can produce at least three tones by working the inner side of the larger of the two always dissimilar claws against a row of teeth on the arm of the same appendage, "much as a man might rub one side of his chest with the palm of the corresponding hand." On the inner side of this crab's chela is to be found the secret of the tones of *Ocypode*, in the shape of a "keyboard," or a row of five transverse striae (Fig. 68, lower). A closer examination discloses that this corrugated keel "is somewhat low, flattened above, with the lower half of its surface moderately broad, the upper half tapering to the end. Near the upper end this area has rather coarse ridges moderately distant from each other; from the upper end downwards to beyond the middle the ridges become gradually finer and more closely set, and on the lower third they are very fine, and the impressions between them extremely narrow." Thus the keyboard has three distinct regions, like a fiddle with three strings; and with the variations and modulations that not only the angle but rapidity of motion may invoke we should realize that *Ocypode macrocera* may have a far greater range of articulate sounds than the unaided human ear is able to appreciate.

In a group of crabs of the genus *Helice*, found in China, the keyboards vary in coarseness of striation in different species, as pictured in Figure 70. These differences in their keyboards surely indicate differences in tone of the sound they produce. Three different yet similar sound producing mechanisms occur in three species of crabs belonging to the genus *Globopilomnus*. Two of these are found in West Africa and adjacent islands; the third is Indo-Pacific in its much wider range. As with *Helice*, even if crabs of a genus 'speak the same language' the 'dialects' of the species are quite different.

FIG. 70. Varieties of Chinese land crab (*Helice tridens*). The sub-orbital stridulating ridge of the upper crab is fine-toothed, that of the middle crab, medium-toothed, and that of the lower, coarse-toothed.

In southeastern Asia and the East Indies there occurs in countless numbers a little globular fellow, *Dotilla myctiroides*. This goes through group evolutions smacking of military maneuvers. The instant danger threatens, these crabs disappear in the moist sand of the beaches, which they use as parade grounds. At a little distance the crabs seem to be intensely blue with bright yellow legs, and their apparently ceaseless maneuvers give to the beach the appearance of an endless shimmering, iridescent sea. But on closer approach, the gaudy spread of pigment resolves itself into myriads of little crabs climbing over one another, three or four deep, in their anxiety to sink from sight as the enemy approaches. The entire performance is accompanied by a continuous wave of sound—a rustling, swishing sound, as of the wind blowing through dry autumn leaves that still hang on the trees; now softer and now louder, as the innumerable host rushes here and there or wheels about. As long as the crabs are in rapid motion the sound continues, only to be stilled with their mystical disappearance.

This massed volume of sound is produced by the brushing of the joints of the ambulatory legs against the edges of the carapace, and, more particularly, against a roughened convoluted area on each side of the much inflated body, which seems to have assumed this shape for the express purpose of allowing the legs to make the sound peculiar to these crabs by brushing over the specially modified lateral walls of the carapace. Here we seem to have an instance of purposeful sound production to give warning of change of movement to all members of the corps.

The fact that many investigators have failed to find any sense of perception that might be called auditory in Crustacea is no proof that these animals do not appreciate sound and sound variations, or that they do not communicate with one another by means of sound. It may be that both in our reasoning and our experimental investigations we fail to "speak their language." The many and varied devices with which Crustacea are equipped for producing sound—or merely noise, if you prefer—and the modulations of tone of which many of these devices are capable surely have a significance that is far from being properly understood.

Carl Aurivillius, in his detailed study of sound production among crustaceans, found reason to believe that it is a form of speech in these animals. He based his opinion on the fact that in most of the crabs in which the stridulating apparatus is most highly developed— such as the ocypodes—the meral joints of the legs are compressed, straight-sided and rather thin and poorly calcified (Fig. 71). The very nature of the fragile walls of these joints renders them sensitive, sound-receptive diaphragms, capable of performing the function for which they were evidently intended. Why else should they be so developed in these crabs? Nor must we overlook the fact that not a few crabs are provided with curious, more or less membranous areas, which, even if located on the meral joints of the ambulatory legs, are inescapably suggestive of a tympanic function. As strangely placed as these "ears" are, they occupy a no more unique position than do the auditory organs of the grasshopper, which are found paired on either side of the first segment of the abdomen.

FIG. 71. Australian sand bubbler (*Scopimera inflata*) showing tympani as dark oval spots on legs. These may represent organs of hearing. After Kinghorn.

At every turn, we seem to come upon another articulate crustacean. The late Clarence R. Shoemaker, former amphipod specialist at the U.S. National Museum, pointed out that even in the rare amphipod genus *Photis*, sound-producing structures are present. Here, a series of closely set ridges on one joint of a pair of appendages can be rubbed across a similar set of ridges on a plate overhanging an adjacent appendage.

The second world war with its widespread submarine activity created a tremendous interest in underwater sounds, and their study was given high priority rating as a research problem. In this connection, we at the National Museum compiled a list of over one hundred records of crustacean sound production from around the world, in all seven seas.

Judging from the wealth of literature on the subject, the interest in crustacean sound has not lagged since the war. But we still have a long way to go before the last word can be said on the "speech" of Crustacea.

VI. Light and Color in Crustaceans

Luminescence

Luminescence in the sea, with its beauty and mystery, involves one of the most fascinating problems of zoology and biochemistry—the production of cold light. Many theories have been advanced to account for it. Even Benjamin Franklin made it the subject of his penetrating curiosity. He believed that it was due to electric sparks generated by friction among the salts of the sea.

Much of the most productive research on the subject has been done on the marine "firefly" of Japan, an ostracod, *Cypridina hilgendorfi*. This small crustacean gives off brilliant rich-blue sparks of light when disturbed and can repeat the act many times. A few individuals of this species shaken up in a tube of water give easily enough light to read by, and if alcohol is substituted for water the light may persist as long as fifteen minutes. Indeed, so powerful are the substances that engender the light that in water a proportion as minute as one part in 1,700,000,000 parts of water will still give a visible light. The ostracods themselves, as well as the

light-producing materials they contain, may be dried
and preserved almost indefinitely. E. Newton Harvey in
his *Bioluminescence* reveals that during World War II,
Japanese officers in the Pacific were able to read vital
messages in the dark of night by the low intensity light
given off by a bit of dry Cypridina powder moistened in
the palm of a man's hand.

I suppose not less than a dozen ostracods are known to
possess this gift of luminescence. The color of the light
they emit varies: in some, like *Cypridina,* it is an intense blue; in others it is bright green or yellow, or a
combination of both. The luminescent secretions of ostracods are produced by special glands, and some of
them can store up considerable quantities of light producing substance. It is supposed that the purpose of the
secretions is to frighten away enemies. This theory is in
keeping with the ostracods' habit of shunning any light
that would render their own less effective. During the
day they lie concealed, and on moonlight nights they
are hard to find. Even the electric illumination of water
fronts where they occur inhibits their activities. Brilliantly luminous ostracods will at times be left stranded,
by the wash of the waves, on the beaches of the Dry
Tortugas; and two species are found in the shallow water
of Montego Bay, Jamaica.

In suitable seasons in San Francisco Bay every dip of
boat oars at night stirs up much shimmery white gold,
for which certain copepods are responsible. Not less than
seven known species of these crustaceans give off light
from organs distributed over the body. *Pleuromma ab-
dominale,* a cosmopolitan species, may have as many as
eighteen such organs. Two species of luminescent copepods are known from the coasts of Norway, Spitzbergen,
and north Greenland, and A. E. Nordenskiöld wrote of
luminescent copepods cast ashore on the Arctic coasts
as follows: "Very singular is the impression experienced
in walking on a cold, dark, winter's day (with the

temperature nearly at the freezing point of mercury) on snow from which on all sides shoot at every step sparkles so vivid that sometimes one is almost afraid of seeing one's boots and clothes catch fire." These sparkles emanate from live copepods, although of course, under the circumstances mentioned, they cannot be free-swimming.

As we go higher in the scale of crustacean life, the light organs change from the simple glands of ostracods and some copepods to organs of greater complexity, and at times these will have a lens as well as a reflector to intensify the light they emit. In the euphausiid malacostracans we find organs of this type so complex that they were long considered eyes, and that they had light-producing functions was not realized till a comparatively recent date.

Many species of luminous Crustacea are pelagic forms, such as our common New England coast species *Meganyctiphanes norvegica,* the individuals of which, during midsummer, swarm along the coast, flashing as brilliantly as so many fireflies. Other species live at greater depths. Colonel Alcock had the good fortune to bring up alive two species of prawns—*Heterocarpus alphonsi* and *Aristeus coruscans*—from a depth of 561 fathoms in the Indian Ocean. Both sexes of *Heterocarpus* "poured out copious clouds of a ghostly blue light of sufficient intensity to illuminate a bucket of sea water so that all its contents were visible in the clearest detail." This light emanated from the prawn's anterior region.

Professor Ulric Dahlgren stated that the luminous substance in these shrimps is "secreted by a large number of glands of the common integumental type found in crustaceans. These glands pour out the secretion from hundreds of tiny, hairlike ducts opening on the underside of the head from around the mouth and from the inner sides of the bases of the limbs on the anterior part of the thorax. This very small amount of secretion is then mixed with the strong stream of water, augmented for the occasion, that comes from the respiratory chamber and is thus carried out in the copious clouds of light that have been described."

Special light-emitting organs in animals are called photophores. There is one shrimp, *Sergestes challengeri,* which when full grown will show as many as a hundred and fifty of these points of light, and we can well imagine that such a crustacean in full illumination would look like Coney Island on the move. No luminous true crabs have as yet been recorded.

As to the whys and wherefores of this light-producing power in marine animals, Professor Franz Doflein summarized as follows the various theories that have been advanced: to attract prey; to attract other individuals of the same species in order to form and maintain swarms; to attract the opposite sex; to frighten off a pursuing enemy by a sudden flash of light, or to confuse him with a luminous mist while the pursued escapes in the dark; and possibly, in the absence of other light to illuminate objects the animal may wish to see.

Dr. Stanley Kemp, in reviewing these theories, remarked:

> It is evident that these suggestions will not account for every case which can be found; the photophores in the roof of the branchial chamber of *Sergestes* remain inexplicable.
>
> The vast majority of marine animals which possess photophores live at the surface or at intermediate depths and never occur on the bottom. . . .
>
> Many of the higher marine animals live on the seafloor at depths to which no ray of sunlight can ever penetrate, and, though they possess well-developed eyes, are themselves, for the most part, without any special illuminating apparatus. That light exists at these depths seems almost certain. It is probably fairly plentiful in regions thickly populated by Coe-

lenterates, and the excretions of numerous animals of a more highly organized nature have been found to be brilliantly phosphorescent. The restriction of photophores to species living in mid-water seems only explicable on the theory that there is a comparatively plentiful supply of light on the bottom itself.

The production of light in these animals, as numerous researches have amply demonstrated, is brought about by the reaction, in the presence of oxygen and moisture, of one photogenic substance—luciferase, which is secreted in special gland cells—on another—luciferin, which is found throughout the tissues of the body and in the blood.

The most remarkable feature of these essential substances is that they may be dried, extracted with ether, or treated in various other ways without affecting their power of producing light. The process, then, is quite independent of the animal body in which the substances were produced and therefore is a physiochemical phenomenon. If kept dry, the substances will retain their light-giving properties for months and even years.

Not all crustacean luminescence is produced at the will of the animal. Sometimes tragedy is involved. One of the unfortunates among the illuminated is *Talitrus,* an amphipod beach hopper, which appears to be subject to infection by luminous bacteria. Without any impairment of their luminous power, the bacteria seem to thrive and flourish within the alimentary tract of the amphipod. Eventually the helpless host succumbs to the inroads of this internal blaze of glory. Other amphipods, if not already infected, may in turn become so if, as is often their wont, they eat their fallen brethren. Such infection is inevitably fatal.

The phosphorescence of aquatic creatures has usually been associated with a salt-water or a sea-beach habitat; but observations have shown that a Japanese fresh-water shrimp, *Xiphocaridina compressa,* glows with inward light just as does the marine amphipod *Talitrus,* and does not long survive the infection which produces it. Even healthy individuals of this species, when placed in fresh water in the laboratory, became luminous in one or two days and died after remaining luminous for several hours. The causative bacterium was described by Dr. Y. Yasaki as new to science, and probably the first luminous bacterium found in fresh water. The light it produced was so intense that that emitted by twenty or thirty of the luminous shrimps in a test tube was sufficient to read by in an otherwise dark room.

There was a time when all marine luminescence was ascribed to bacteria; but nowadays, as has already been shown, it is known that bacteria are not responsible for this quality in all sea animals that possess it. There are certain fish and cephalopods which have special organs, or culture chambers, for carrying stores of this bacterial light without harm to themselves. Some make use of it in screening their escape by a mantle of light—paradoxical as this may sound—and others as a lure for food.

Light is a most efficient means of attracting all kinds of animals and is employed wherever feasible by the careful and thorough collector of marine organisms. Fishermen since earliest times have used torches and lighted fagots for attracting their catch, and this method is still extensively employed in many parts of the world.

Color

The remarkable phenomenon of light in Crustacea finds what is almost its peer in another phenomenon—that of color. Many crustaceans, like some other animals, seem able to change their color at will.

The shrimp *Hippolyte varians* has this gift to a high degree. Any number of individuals of this species will rest upon red or green or other-colored seaweed and be

practically indistinguishable even to a very close observer. It is true that the facility with which they
change from one color to another seems to vary with
age. A very young one can change from red to green—
to match a green background—in a few hours, but such
a change takes longer and longer as the animal grows
older. It appears that early in life these shrimps make
their choice of habitat and color and later tend to abide
by it. Those that make their home upon the green weeds
take on a livery of like color, and those living among the
red or the brown weeds dress themselves accordingly.
But one may force an older individual to change color
by placing him in quite a different environment. When
this is done, with few exceptions the shrimp will respond
in time; and thereafter it is easier for him to reverse or
change color. One change all shrimps, whether young or
old and whatever their fixed color, make every night:
they turn blue. Quite the reverse of rational humans,
Hippolyte turns night into day for feeding and repose.
He spends the hours of sunshine resting and sleeping
and in the vegetative manufacture and storing up of fat,
and it is during the day that his wonderful mimicry of
the background takes place. *Hippolyte*'s pallette carries
but three pigments—red, yellow, and blue; but by expansion and contraction of the chromatophores, these primary colors are wonderfully suppressed and intermingled
as required.

Professor Frank A. Brown, Jr., a leading American
investigator of color changes, has found that the variety
of color phases of the Gulf-weed shrimp *Latreutes fuco-
rum,* rivals that described for the *Hippolyte*. He reports that some, colored pale yellow, yellowish-green,
greenish-brown, brown, or red, reproduce the diverse
colors of algae to which they cling. Others are mottled,
striped, or barred to correspond in pattern to irregularly
colored bits of weeds. And still others are black or black
with white spots and resemble the purple-black lifeless
tips of algae together with the encrusting bryozoans.

Victor Bauer devoted much study to the crustacean life of the Mediterranean meadows of sea-grass. Among the roots and root stalks of the grass he found concealed the tubes of the tube-building amphipods; and in the sandy stretches between the patches of vegetation were portunid crabs, resting on or half buried in the sand, but speckled and mottled so like the pattern on the sandy bottom made by the play of light and shade as to be well-nigh indistinguishable from it. On the leaves of the grass he found isopods and shrimps, which followed even the seasonal change of the sea-grass in their choice of livery: in the spring, when all the new shoots were fresh and green, so were all the crustaceans that lived in their shelter or upon them; but later, as the leaves turned brown, the crustaceans did likewise.

The well-known amphipod, *Hyperia galba,* is quite adept in the art of mimicry. It travels around attached to the transparent bells or umbrellas of jellyfish, and at such times it is devoid of color, matching closely its means of transportation; but when free from the jellyfish it rapidly takes on a yellowish or brownish tone, more like the sea bottom on which it happens to come to rest.

Color is protective—no doubt about it—when it matches and merges with its background or environment. The speckled birds of the sea beach are well-known examples of protective coloring, and crustaceans of varied habitat take their place with them. Yet investigations tend to show that protection is not the primary function of color in some animals at least. Professors Frederick Keeble and F. W. Gamble examined one hypothesis after another in an effort to account for the presence of the color-bearing chromatophores in *Hippolyte* and to discover their function and the reasons for their changes and behavior in different individuals of the species. They found a fat-synthesizing function paramount. While *Hippolyte* rests by day on the sea plants of its surroundings, fat is produced under the influence of the sun's rays. Their hypothesis is not so difficult of proof as one might think. When animals are starved in the dark, the fat globules—along with the pigments in the chromatophores—become gradually depleted, just as green plants get pale in the absence of light; but "if such lean specimens are taken out again into the light at the end of a fortnight, they will in the course of a single day show not only a fatty skin, but a far denser accumulation of fat than is to be seen in a freshly caught prawn."

The discovery of the sinus gland in the eyestalks of Crustacea by Bertil Hanstrom of the University of Lund, Sweden, and the relationship of its function to color changes and molting led to further discoveries concerning the way in which color responses are controlled. A crustacean may have all or some of the responsible color pigments, (chromoproteins) of which, according to the biochemists, there are some twenty or more. These are contained in the chromatophore cells which house the pigment masses. The monochromatic chromatophores in the main have names corresponding to their contained pigments: red, erythrophores; yellow, xanthophores; white, guanophores; black or brown, melanophores. In prawns and shrimps polychromatic chromatophores containing several pigments are especially numerous. These make possible the adaptive changes of such crustaceans to background patterns and color. Although crustaceans do synthesize various chromoproteins, only photosynthetic plants can synthesize the yellow pigments, the carotenoids. Crustaceans come by these by eating foods containing them. This is also true of chlorophyll, the green of leaves and plants. Not a crustacean chromoprotein, chlorophyll may lend its color to crustaceans ingesting it. Chlorophyllous materials, as well as carotenoids, become metabolized within the crustacean's alimentary tract, serving in part as nourishment, and in part becoming synthesized into pigment-forming materials and even vitamins.

Blue is a color not infrequently met with in Crustacea, as in *Hippolyte* at night, and occasionally in lobsters and crayfish. Related to the yellow carotenoid pigments, crustacean blue is a carotenoid-protein complex that is said to form no lasting chromatophores.

The transport of oxygen within the crustacean body falls to the lot of the haemoglobins and the haemocyanins, metal-containing proteins which, however, do not give a general coloration to our crustaceans. The former derives its red color from iron, the latter its blue color from copper. Haemocyanin, long associated with Crustacea, is narrowly restricted to the Decapoda and Stomatopoda. Haemoglobin is more widely distributed among Crustacea other than Malacostraca—branchiopods, ostracods, copepods, and barnacles. Because of its great affinity for oxygen this iron-containing protein seems especially to be favored by lower Crustacea living in evanescent puddles of often poorly oxygenated water.

Hormonal or endocrine secretions of the sinus gland and more recently discovered 'X-organ' together with the so-called neuro-secretory tracts in the "brain" and ganglia of the crustacean nervous system vary or control the degree of expansion and spotting of the several or individual pigments within the cells—much as an impressionistic painter might produce color effect or pattern on his canvas. It is questionable whether crustaceans can produce a certain color effect by desire or will; however, those which do undergo change in color or pattern seem quite able to respond to external conditions—and perhaps reflect emotional states in so doing.

Reviewing here the subject of color, one cannot fail to be impressed with the importance of color in one form or another in the life and well being of Crustacea. Their pigments or chromoproteins are certainly multipurpose substances. In various combinations and situations they may produce color patterns, protective or indicative of emotional states, or of sexual maturity; and though the lines are not always clearly drawn, they also serve metabolic functions—such as the production of fat.

VII. Crustaceans as Food and Medicine

It was recorded during early colonial days in New England that "the least boy in the (Salem) plantation may catch and eat what he will" of lobsters. Let us hope that this early representative of impecunious youth realized his good fortune and made the most of it. For it is long since unlimited supplies of lobster have been accessible to any of us, let alone the least of us. It seems hardly credible that there was a time when the mackerel fishermen, whose lines the lobsters robbed of bait, regarded them as pests. And not only were they plentiful: they were large. Twenty-five pounders were not uncommon.

In 1892 the fishery yielded almost 24,000,000 pounds of lobsters, valued at $1,062,392. Thirteen years later the annual yield had fallen to half its former weight, but with a value of $1,364,721. Production stayed at about that level for thirty-five years. The price of lobster, like the cost of living, climbed steadily, and the value of the 1942 lobster fishery was well over twice that of 1905. But not until the late 1940's did the catch top the twelve million pounds of the early 1900's. In the last few years production has run between twenty-eight and twenty-nine million pounds. This in monetary value to the industry is well over $14,000,000. Though lobsters now average no more than a pound in weight, these "chicken lobsters" are in demand today because of their tender flesh and relatively low price. Before the years of intensive fishing the average trapped lobsters were twice and in some years three times as heavy as these one-pounders.

The blue-crab fishery of the Chesapeake Bay region alone yielded a catch of over seventy-four million pounds in 1961. This toothsome seafood reaches the market in the form of the familiar hard-shell crabs and the much relished soft-shelled one, for the latter form is nothing more than the blue crab in a state of molt. The soft-shelled crab harvest for Chesapeake Bay as a whole totals between two-and-a-half and three million pounds a year. If to the blue crab production we add the New England green and rock crabs and the South Atlantic and Gulf Coast stone crabs, the U.S. east coast total of commercially taken crabs came to 152 million pounds, valued at nearly $8,500,000.

Comparable fishery on the west coast, California to Alaska, is based on the Dungeness crab, *Cancer magister*. In 1961 close to thirty-three million pounds were taken, valued at nearly $4,000,000. Because of its different habits, this crab never comes to market in the soft shell condition.

Perhaps the most spectacular of the American crab fisheries is that of the North Pacific king crab, *Paralithodes camtschatica*. This species ranges on our side of the Pacific from the Gulf of Alaska to the Bering Sea. Starting from scratch in the early forties, this fishery recently returned a record annual catch of over forty-three million pounds.

Formerly blue crabs were caught chiefly on trot-lines—long lines with baited leaders laid on the bottoms where crabs would overrun them. When the crab took hold of the bait he would be drawn to the surface and dip-net wafted to the fisherman's boat. Crab pots or traps now have pretty much replaced trot-lines in the commercial fishery, with a marked improvement in the size of the catch. In Chesapeake Bay in the winter months the blue crabs resort largely to the lower reaches of the bay, more or less to hibernate in the muddy-sand and weedy bottoms. During this time metal dredges are employed to drag up the reluctant crustaceans.

The Florida stone crab fishery is a sizeable industry, and while more limited, is also an active one in other South Atlantic and Gulf States. Crab pots are used, but a lot of these *Menippes* are still taken by hand. In going after them, the uninitiated or unwary should take warning. Though the crab is sluggish and not particularly pugnacious, its powerful claws can easily crush a finger. These crabs like to burrow in shallow areas below the low tide mark and are fond of digging in and about seawalls, withdrawing into fortuitous holes and crevices among or under the rocks composing them.

The Andalusians usually catch burrowing crabs by thrusting a pointed stick in the ground beneath the animal to cut off its retreat when it is observed in the upper portion of its dwelling. This method is almost universally used, but the crabbers of Sarasota Bay, working over harder ground, secure *Menippe* by poking a stout iron rod into the holes. Stone crabs, being the bulldogs among Crustacea, lay hold of the rod with such a powerful and tenacious grip that they may be drawn forth from their retreat and secured before they let go.

In Chile, natives on the west coast of Patagonia employ a simple device for catching long-legged lithodid crabs, relatives of our northern King crab (Fig. 72). The summer is the season when crabs are more easily taken, for they come to shallow water to breed. Fishermen first catch a female crab with line and bait. Having got her, they attach her firmly in a noose and lower her into the water. The male crabs are ardent wooers, and five or six

FIG. 72. Chilean lithodid crab (*Lithodes antarctica*). Grows to be six-and-a-quarter inches in body length.

will so firmly embrace the tethered female on each immersion that they can be drawn to the surface and picked off; the love lure can then be used again.

The large claw of stone crab is the portion most commonly eaten; large and heavy, it contains a delicious morsel of flesh. The Sarasota Bay fishermen seem to make common practice of breaking off this claw and throwing the crab back. Thus it is permitted to live in order to provide the market with another claw the next year—for it takes a year to grow a new one. Surprisingly enough, the claw that begins to grow, molt by molt, after the injury, to replace the one that was sacrificed as food for man, is the opposite and smaller claw; and it continues to grow until it approximates the size and appearance of the original large claw. At the same time the newly formed claw appearing where the big one was removed becomes a new small claw.

Crustaceans themselves seem aware that their limbs may be broken off fairly easily. The chief endeavor of fighting fiddlers appears to be to wrest off the opponent's large claw. And the robber crab, like man, amputates the greater chela of certain crabs to eat. On Christmas Island this crab has been observed quite regularly to chase the burrowing land crab to its retreat. Once safely within its home, the *Cardisoma* defensively sticks out its large claw. Apparently this is just the reaction the *Birgus* is anticipating; forthwith he seizes the chela, wrenches it off, and hastens away with the tasty morsel.

Among the crustaceans highly regarded as an article of table fare are shrimps. As a result important shrimp fisheries have grown up in many parts of the world. The over-all United States catch in the record year 1954 amounted to 268 million pounds. These were taken with a variety of gear, but the bulk was gotten by means of trawls. The American consumption of headless shrimp in 1964 rose to a total of 287 million pounds, U.S. production plus imports.

Mixed in with the Gulf of Mexico shrimp catches usually are a number of four to six inch long mantis shrimp or "Squillas," variously called "nurse shrimp" or "Shrimp Mammies." They are not put on sale in the States, but packing shed hands sometimes take them home to cook and eat. I learned how delicious these shrimp could be during the 1957 Smithsonian-Bredin Expedition to the French Society Islands. In Bora Bora we purchased several from a local fisherman. Compared to Gulf Coast mantis shrimp they were large specimens —ten to twelve inches in length. One eats the "tail," which cooked, had a sweet taste and proved to be about the most toothsome piece of crustacean flesh imaginable.

The delicate, transparent opossum shrimp form the basis of a very considerable but comparatively unknown fishery in the English Channel, and no doubt the industry has there been prosecuted in much the same manner and for the same purpose since the Norman Conquest— and perhaps before. The Island of Jersey is the scene of this fishery; and there the mysids are compounded into a paste called *cherve*, which is sold to mullet anglers for bait. In the Orient, species of mysids closely related to the Jersey shrimp are used as human food.

Crayfish, also, must be classed as edible crustaceans, for they are consumed abroad in prodigious numbers. As long ago as the time of the Roman Empire they were held in high esteem, although as a rule in those days they were the food of the poorer classes. The slaves ate the crayfish just as they were caught—that is, without giving them any preliminary care; but those destined for the tables of the elect, including the royal table, were first fattened in earthenware pots designed for the purpose. And in this country today, freshwater crayfish are held in high esteem and consumed in quantity along the Gulf Coast, the Mississippi River and in the Pacific Northwest. The crayfish catch in the United States in 1962 totaled nearly 2,300,000 pounds, which were valued at $411,000.

Man is not the only animal to which crayfish are acceptable as food. Snakes, salamanders, raccoons, otters, alligators, and certain birds relish their flesh. John James Audubon left an interesting account—worthy of repetition here—illustrating the intelligence of the white ibis in catching the burrowing crayfish, *Cambarus diogenes.* The bird approaches the mud chimney of intended repast and so breaks up the painstakingly constructed cylinder of clay that some of the debris falls within to notify the dweller that repairs are in order above. With a foreknowledge of what will take place, the bird withdraws a little and awaits the outcome. The poor, diligent crayfish, as soon as everything seems quiet above, begins to clean the extraneous mud and matter from within and to carry it to the surface to restore his broken chimney. There, of course, he meets his fate, and once again the ibis has stilled the pangs of hunger.

Man nowhere makes a practice of eating the minute crustaceans—such as copepods—which abound in the seas and make up so much of the bill of fare of many fish and other aquatic animals. But on at least one occasion tiny amphipods were all that stood between twenty-five men and death. These men made up the Greely Expedition to the Arctic, which ended so tragically over eighty years ago.

With supplies for only a year or two at the most, the expedition passed three years in the Arctic and lost eighteen members of its original complement. The seven rescued owed their lives to the amphipods, as a few extracts from the log of the expedition will show. The first man died on January 18, 1884. We have pieced out the subsequent story from General Greely's account, which we give herewith, largely in his own words:

> March 5. The last of our seal blubber, corn, tomatoes, potatoes, and soup issued today—what shall we do in a few days?
>
> March 16. Brainard made an improvement on my plan of last autumn to dredge for mussels, and suggests that we try and catch shrimps. Certainly our men are full of devices, and we shall yet make a brave fight for our lives.
>
> March 21. A net was made in which to catch shrimps; an improvement of Rice's plan of yesterday.

(These nets were improvised from iron barrel hoops and pieces of sacking and were first baited with such bones and meat scraps as could be spared. Later, as the stringency became greater and greater, little puckers of sealskin, sometimes sewed over stones and fastened into the crude net with the inner side up, served as bait. The whole idea was born of Brainard's observing that countless numbers of amphipods completely devoured every scrap of offal that was thrown in the water.)

> March 23. Rice, indefatigable as ever, was out at 3 a.m. for shrimps. Unfortunately he overturned his net, and brought in only a few ounces.
>
> March 25. The shrimps are now mixed with our stews, and are quite palatable. The minute animals have opened up to us a new avenue of escape.

March 27. Rice made four trips, and succeeded in getting twelve pounds of shrimps.

March 28. Rice was very successful, and got twenty-seven pounds of shrimps.

April 5. Christiansen died.

April 6. Lynn died.

April 9. Rice died.

April 9. Lockwood died.

April 12. Jewell died.

Brainard was very successful in bringing in twenty or thirty pounds of shrimps daily, thus enabling us, with a few ounces of meat, to keep body and soul together.

April 29. Jens was ᐟ accidentally drowned while out trying to get a seal.

May 18. Very stormy last night and this morning. I heard a raven croaking this morning and called Long, who succeeded in killing him. Gave Long the liver, and concluded to use the bird for shrimp bait, thinking we could obtain more from him that way than in eating.

May 19. Ellis died, the first death from starvation in six weeks.

May 22. It is now eight days since our last regular food was issued.

May 23. Ralston died. Brainard got only ten pounds of shrimps, less by far than we are eating. It is a sad state of affairs, and the end must be near.

May 24. Whisler died. For dinner we had a handful of saxifrage, two or three spoonsful of shrimp, and a pint and a half of tea. The cook was caught unfairly dividing our wretched shrimps, giving equal soup but keeping too great a portion of shrimps, and I ordered him relieved as cook. Of the party, at present seven are helpless.

May 26. The storm was so bad this morning that Brainard could not go shrimping, but this afternoon he got eight pounds. Owing to his failure to get shrimps we had a stew last night and this morning of deer thongs, which have been used in lashing together the sledge and for similar purposes.

May 27. Israel died.

June 1. Kislingbury died.

June 3. Salor died.

June 4. Henry, the cook, caught stealing shrimps again.

June 5. Brainard got only five pounds of shrimps.

June 6. More shrimp stealing. Henry, the culprit, shot.

June 6. Bender died.

Dr. Pavy died.

June 7. All the shrimps left were eaten for breakfast.

June 12. Gardiner died.

June 14. Today three years since the expedition sailed from Baltimore.

June 15. Brainard gets few shrimps.

The journal ends June 21.

June 23, all but dead, the seven miserable survivors were rescued by Commander Schley, later the Admiral of Spanish war fame. Seven left of twenty-five, and those seven owed their lives to "shrimps," the tiny amphipods so plentiful in northern waters. General Brainard told me that they got, all told, perhaps fifteen hundred pounds of them.

Other crustaceans likewise, less well known than lobsters, crabs, and true shrimps, may be classed as human food, since they are used for this purpose in many parts of the world. Such are the barnacles and the mantis shrimps or "Squillas," earlier referred to as split-thumbs and often so-called because they do just that when carelessly handled.

There is a large consumption of barnacles in Chile (Fig. 73); and Chile is the home also of another popular

FIG. 73. Aged European edible lobster (*Homarus gammarus*) much overgrown with barnacles. After Schensky.

and unique product of the sea, a deep-water galatheid considerably larger than the more pelagically inclined "lobster krill" favored by baleen whales of the eastern Pacific and Antipodean seas. This species, *Cervimunida johni,* is fished up from depths of as great as two hundred fathoms. It grows to be nearly four inches long. Until 1934 it was considered a very rare species; but somewhat later it began to appear as a novelty seafood in Chilean restaurants. The growth of this newly developed fishery in recent years has been phenomenal. We find the tails of these sizeable galatheids on sale—under the Spanish name "langostinos" (little lobsters)—frozen and canned in chain stores and supermarkets. Of the total Chilean "harvest" of something like seventeen million pounds, the United States imports more than eight hundred thousand pounds frozen and a quarter million pounds canned.

Thus it will be seen that no summing up of the sources of human food is complete which does not include Crustacea; and from my own observations I should say that all members of the class should be included, as

I know of no crustacean in the fresh, unspoiled state that is poisonous or otherwise unfit for human consumption after cooking. Since I so expressed myself—an opinion I still hold—several friends have called my attention to references to poisonous crabs which escaped me during my search of literature.

The first and earliest of these references was Georgius Exerhardus Rumphius' natural history of the island of Amboina (now a part of Indonesia), published in 1705. Most of the crustaceans he described can be identified with present day species. One, "Cancer Rubris Oculis" and another, "Cancer Noxius" are believed to be the names he gave to the same widely distributed Indo-Pacific *Eriphia sebana*. The story which Rumphius relates is that a woman and her daughter ate "Cancer Noxius" and died. But from that far off day to the very present there seems to have been no more than hearsay regarding the incident. No other fatality seems ever to have been reported, nor does it seem that the matter has ever been investigated.

In a very recent picture book of Hawaiian Crustacea there is a large, eight inches across the back, sponge bearing crab *Dromidiopsis*, a relative of our east coast *Dromia*. Of this crab the author says, "In spite of its large size, this crab is not regarded as edible, in fact some fishermen even refer to it as the 'poison crab.'" Here again hearsay, unverified, seems to be repeated.

The only other poisonous crab of which I have heard is the English pea crab, *Pinnotheres pisum*. Commensal in mussels, this was given a bad name by some early naturalists. But just as early the crab had its defender, Thomas Pennant. In his British Zoology (1777), following a brief description of the crab Pennant wrote: "Inhabits the mussel, and unjustly has acquired the repute of being poisonous. The swelling after eating is wholly constitutional; for one that is affected by it, hundreds remain uninjured." Over indulgence even in mussel meats can produce unhappy results, crab or no crab. Also, the mussels could have been at fault: in California, where they are plentiful, one is advised not to partake of them out of season.

Reports should be investigated thoroughly before unfamiliar crabs are eaten—unless the natives and the market place give them a clean bill of health. If these crabs are as dangerous as some may think, more should be known about them.

By and large, it appears that crustaceans are a health-giving food. Recent medical findings reveal that iodine in an organic combination yields better results than iodine in the form of the inorganic salts. All sea foods, including of course marine crustaceans, contain iodine, in this desirable form, and glycogen, the organic reserve for nourishing the animal and building the exoskeleton when moulting. The flesh of the northern lobster is said to "sit well" with weak stomachs. The mitten crab relished by the Chinese is rich in vitamin B_2. *Scylla* and *Portunus* dishes are used for convalescing malaria patients and by asthma sufferers. *Parathelphusa* soup is used for colds. And so crustaceans assume a new value for man: they can be a source of medicine and of vitamins, as well as food. But much of their therapeutic value long and widely believed in some parts of the world is lacking in scientific or biomedical proof.

Geologists working in China, for instance, have learned that fossil crabs are rare finds; this is largely because of the high estimate placed on their medicinal properties by the natives. Innumerable virtues are credited to these petrified crabs. They are considered an excellent antidote for neutralizing all kinds of mineral, metallic, and vegetable poisons. They are also highly regarded as a vermifuge, a most necessary remedy in a country so overrun with human parasites as is China. These fossil crabs are also believed efficacious in curing opacity and other affections of the eye.

From Pliny we gather that the ancients also had several strange uses for river crabs. Freshly macerated and swallowed with water or in the form of ash of the burned crab, they were considered an antidote for all poisons, especially when taken in ass's milk.

Even our own ancestors of no very distant generation prescribed live crustaceans in certain maladies. And they were not crabs or shrimps, either, but the little isopods called sow-bugs or pill-bugs, which are found in damp cellars or under boards in the back yard. The pill-bug acquired its common name from its resemblance, when curled up, to a pill and from its use in former times as one.

In western Europe a few centuries ago every human ill, from heart affection to cancer and from club feet to scrofula, was supposed to yield to the magic of crayfish "eyes." The crayfish or crab eyes are little natural concretions, rounded discoidal nodules of whitish limy matter, laid down in concentric rings on each side of the animal's stomach. The primary purpose for the secretion of these nodules seems to be to furnish the newly molted animal with a readily available store of calcareous material with which quickly to make its new shell as hard and stiff as the outgrown one. To the uninitiated these eyes or stones are considered charms or luck stones. Even in this day and time we receive them at the Museum for determination, and as often as we receive them we are interrogated as to their medicinal property.

In Jamaica there exists a local superstition that the fiddler crab can cure deafness and earache, and it is called, therefore, the "deaf-ear" crab. The treatment consists in crushing the live crab and pouring the juice thus obtained into the afflicted ear.

In Korea the raw juice pressed from river crayfish is used therapeutically in cases of fever and diarrhea. The results, however, are lamentable and frequently fatal.

Crayfishes as well as freshwater crabs, of which Koreans, Japanese, Chinese and others eat great quantities, are the intermediate hosts of the extremely prevalent lung fluke occurring almost everywhere in the Orient. Unless these hosts are thoroughly cooked they will pass on the parasite to whoever eats them. Dogs, cats, and other carnivorous animals, as well as man, become infected; and in countries where the lung fluke is prevalent it is a greater scourge than the hookworm. Not only does it invade the lungs, producing a chronic cough, blood spitting, and an anemic condition, but it penetrates the brain as well, giving rise to all manner of curious afflictions that have been variously diagnosed as infantile paralysis, cerebral hemorrhage, encephalitis, and the like. I cannot stress too strongly the danger of eating these crabs of the Orient when not thoroughly cooked— or of eating, in infected districts, any uncooked food which has been washed in water, or even drinking unboiled water.

Even the tiny Entomostraca loom large in medical annals as intermediate hosts of a number of unpleasant parasites. Napoleon's soldiers in Egypt were troubled by a pernicious "guinea worm," which they got from drinking water carrying its intermediate host—the fresh water copepod, *Cyclops*, which is found in India, Arabia, and Africa.

And our own Great Lakes region has been invaded by the fish tape of Europe, *Diphyllobothrium*. Like the guinea worm, it makes use of the fresh-water *Cyclops* as an intermediate host, spending part of its life in this crustacean, another part (the second larval stage) in fish, and the balance in whatever vertebrate offers—be it man, feline, canine, or water bird. The danger to man in regions where this tapeworm occurs lies only in eating infected fish without first thoroughly cooking it.

VIII. The Sins of Crustaceans

It may seem rather cavalier treatment of the Crustacea to save the account of their sins—from the human point of view—to the last. By so doing we appear perhaps to convict our friendship of hypocrisy, in view of all the praise previously heaped upon them. But the tale will probably not rob the epicure of his taste for soft-shelled crabs, nor the student of his newly aroused admiration for the class as a whole. And the sins of Crustacea, like the sins of some great men, make up some of the most interesting parts of their biographies.

The earliest recorded account—as far as I know—dealing with the economic conflict of crabs and men was written in China in the sixth century B.C. A wise counselor of the then king of Yeuh (now the province of Chekiang) warned his master that he should abandon his warlike preparations because of the ravages of the rice crab, "that spared for man not a seed (of rice) in late years."

In India there are nearly a dozen different species of crabs causing appreciable damage to rice and the fields where it is grown. Some attack the tender young shoots;

others seem to fell the standing grain, or else—in fields located on the sea coasts—so to weaken, by their burrowing, the dikes that impound the water necessary to the plants that salt water is let in. What is worse, and also more common, the burrows of the crabs drain the fields and expose the tender grain to the devastating heat of the tropical sun. In Ceylon, where rice is grown on terraces along the hillsides, the crabs weaken the bunds, or dikes; and the continued rains of the long wet season complete their destruction. The breaks not only allow the water to escape and the rich soil to be washed away, but they are also the cause of the young plants in the paddy below becoming overwhelmed with silt and dirt.

Poisoning has been tried to combat crab pests in rice fields; but the poison is apt to become too dilute, in the presence of so much water, to have much effect. Trapping the fellows in rotund, wide-mouthed jars has proved successful in Ceylon. The pots, baited with boiled rice bran, are buried three or four inches below the level of the water, where they are readily sought out by the crabs; and once in the globe-shaped pots, they can't climb out. Once in Mandalay, in rice fields covering sixteen acres, twenty thousand crabs were so potted during the two months of the year when the young sprouts are most subject to damage. The natives have discovered that the crabs are more active during or just after a rain than at other times and that they can rouse them from their burrows by beating on the ground with a switch to simulate the fall of rain. When the fields are drained for harvesting, and in the dry season particularly, the crabs tend to hibernate: in the course of well digging they have been uncovered at depths of five and six feet, comfortably ensconced in pockets of moist mud.

Udang ketak, as the natives call him, is the miscreant that damages the bunds of the rice fields in the Federated Malay States. He is the shrimplike *Thalassina ano-*

mala. Very numerous in the mud of tidal areas, shrimps of this species dig large, ramifying burrows many yards in length and extending downward at least to low-tide level. In the excavation of these subways, the earth which is passed out takes on the shape of mounds, which reach the astonishing height of two feet or more. So numerous are they that in some places walking is impeded, each large hillock being so close to its neighbor that it is difficult to find a footing among them. Along muddy coasts, where the *Thalassina* are at home, these mounds are a conspicuous feature of the landscape. In the rice-growing sections of their range, these shrimps are prime pests, tunneling the bunds in all directions and letting in salt water at high tide. Lime placed in the burrows is an effective poison temporarily but is not a permanent deterrent. Moreover, too much of it is harmful to the rice fields. A more lasting deterrent is a layer of the tough fibrous bases of palm tree leaves, soaked in coal tar and laid on top of the bunds before the final foot of earth is placed on them. Until recently it was believed that these shrimps fed on rice plants, but Dr. D. S. Johnson of the University of Malaya has pointed out that the alimentary tract of *Thalassina* is packed with mud, and that the animal derives its nourishment from the organic content of the mud through which it thrusts its way.

The province of Valencia, in Spain, is a great rice growing district, and there *Triops* makes depredations on the rice plants. *Triops* is a little fellow, a couple of inches long, and looks like a baby horseshoe crab. In Spanish the name is *tortugueta*—little turtle. Occurring at times in enormous numbers, they stir up the fine silt in which the rice is planted, expose the roots and kill so many young plants that they become a serious menace. An American relative, *Triops longicaudatus,* overran extensive rice fields in California in the late 1940's. Uncovering the roots and upsetting the rice seedlings as they "ploughed" the bottoms of the fields in search of food, they so muddied the water that sunlight could not reach the plants (Fig. 74). *Triops* thrives on a variety of foods found in the mud—bacteria, protozoa, small worms, insect larvae, *Daphnia,* even fairy shrimp, and its own kind if injured or small and helpless.

FIG. 74. *Triops* at work in California rice fields. From Rosenberg.

Draining the fields would kill *Triops* or carry it off—but an even greater evil would result, for flocks of birds await just such an opportunity to get at the rice. Then too, draining the fields is not effective unless they are allowed to remain dry for a short time, for large numbers of *Triops* survive in very shallow puddles. Moreover, when dry fields are reflooded unwanted water weeds may get a troublesome start. It is better to poison these crustacean pests as they succumb to quite dilute solutions of chloride of lime, sodium cyanide, or ammonium chloride. In California, a one hundred acre field dusted with copper sulphate at the rate of twelve pounds per acre resulted in a complete kill in four days with no injury to the rice plants. *Triops* is still a pest, but not so great a problem as formerly, due to the selectivity of copper sulphate and its low toxicity to wildlife. More powerful insecticides work effectively but must be applied with extreme caution because of their adverse effect on other animal life in the area.

The successful growing of rice in Puerto Rico is also jeopardized by crustacean pests. Here the Department of Agriculture has been trying to combat the large gray land crabs, *Cardisoma*, which can wipe out whole fields of the grain at one fell swoop. The fields where rice can be grown are formed by raising low dikes on ground underlaid by a clay stratum, impervious to water. But the crabs, which burrow by nature, seem to find the rice fields ideal places for opening new subdivisions; and once they penetrate the water-retaining layer of clay, the water goes through it as readily as it would through a gigantic sieve or colander. These same fellows are found in southern Florida (Fig. 75), where they are inordinately fond of the sprouting tomato plants and nip

FIG. 75. Male land crab (*Cardisoma*) and burrows. Courtesy of the Bureau of Biological Survey.

them off as soon as they poke their way above the surface of the ground. The number of crabs infesting these tomato lands may run from five to ten thousand an acre. To eliminate them costs from fifteen to forty dollars an acre, the lower figure applying to previously untilled ground. They present no simple problem, especially when they can scale a thirty-inch cement retaining wall with apparently little difficulty. But then, again, these are no little fellows, for one has been seen in Dade County, Florida, with a maximum spread of twenty-two inches.

Crustacea are also among the list of animals that prey on the much harassed cotton plant, particularly in the Mississippi delta region. Here it is the crayfish that cuts down the sprouting plants; and, like the land crab needs to be laid low with poison in his burrow, carbon bisulphide being chiefly employed for this purpose. As we examine the Yearbook of the United States Department of Agriculture for 1911, we can but be astounded by the destruction then wrought by these crustaceans. We read, "Over a wide stretch of country, estimated at not less than one thousand square miles, crawfish prevent to a very considerable extent the successful production of cotton and corn. They do the greatest amount of damage just after the plant appears and before the secondary leaves are developed. Large fields of young cotton have been destroyed in a single night. Corn also is extensively eaten, but is not so bady damaged as cotton."

Agricultural enterprises may suffer wherever land crabs abound, unless they are guarded against or poisoned; yet the crabs may help as well as hinder the farmer in his endeavors, because they are natural tillers of the land. They are veritable ten-footed earthworms with an enormous capacity for work. They turn over the soil more thoroughly than man could possibly do, even with all the machines he has devised to aid him. Also the crabs are efficient scavengers of animal and plant refuse, and as they work in great armies they clear away immense quantities of objectionable waste in a remarkably short time. This service is particularly valuable in the tropics, where it is essential to man's health that decaying matter be quickly disposed of.

An epidemic of terrestial isopods which occurred in Holland is possibly the most striking one the world has known. A colorless or whitish continental species, *Haplophthalmus danicus*, was at one time reported in such enormous numbers in *Portulaca* gardens that the ground was actually white with them. Various means may be employed to keep down these pests. Poison baits made of potatoes—of which the sow-bugs are inordinately fond—sprinkled with Paris green and London purple have proved most effective.

Another isopod—the pill-bug, or sow-bug—also does much damage. Though feasting chiefly on decaying or fallen trees or other plants, pill-bugs often show a predilection for living plants. In fact, in all temperate parts of the earth, if they occur in numbers, their food seems to embrace the greater part of the vegetable kingdom. A fernery in England was once practically ruined by a little fellow as red as the last word of his name—*Trichoniscus roseus*. The place was so overrun with the pests that it had to be taken down—rock work and all—and rebuilt, and the old, infested soil carted away.

The terrestrial amphipod *Talitrus* that normally lives in damp surroundings in more or less tropic regions also has been reported from greenhouses in Europe and America.

In Florida and the Gulf States where two species of *Talitrus* have become established, they have proved quite seasonal, becoming most abundant after warm rains with concomitant periods of high humidity, moving about freely and on occasion invading houses along the Gulf Coast in Texas and Florida. They are more of a nuisance than a pest, and insecticides such as DDT sprinkled in places where they congregate should prove an effective deterrent. Dr. E. L. Bousfield of the National Museum of Canada has reported that this amphipod is now absent from Canadian greenhouses, where it was common a generation ago, as the result of judicious applications of that insecticide.

Oyster farming suffers from crustaceans in much the same way that ordinary farming does. A near relative of *udang ketak* of the Federated Malay States exacts a heavy tribute from the Puget Sound oyster growers. The *Callianassa*, however, are exclusively marine in habit. In the state of Washington the oysters are grown in shallow "pans" of water shut in by low retaining walls of concrete. In order to obtain a constant supply of fresh water as well as to secure for themselves a safe retreat, the *Callianassa* extend their subterranean burrows under these walls, thus allowing the water in the pans to escape and exposing the young oysters to the fatal heat of the sun. Even where the burrows do not undermine the walls and drain off the water, the operations of these doughty excavators are apt to smother with silt all the oyster spat within range. Fine silt will suffocate oysters in their infancy, whereas an older oyster would be but temporarily annoyed until the next tide cleared the atmosphere for him.

In France *Carcinus maenas* is a reputed enemy of oysters. The French oystermen have observed it detaching, with its chelae, the young spat from plants or other objects, breaking the shells and devouring the contents. Over here where *Carcinus* is our common New England green crab, it has in some sections been accused of having about killed off the soft-shelled clam *Mya arenaria*, a highly prized seafood since Colonial times, especially in the Gulf of Maine where the crab was unknown before 1930. The responsibility for the decline of the clam population, however, has to be shared with the swimming crab, *Callinectes*, the marine arachnid *Limulus*, and the fisherman. Though mostly caught for bait, Carcinus is usually served in restaurants when broiled soft-shelled crab is ordered, according to Dr. Donald Zinn, the University of Rhode Island. The annual catch of green crabs in each of the last several years has totaled between sixty and seventy thousand pounds.

Of the depredations of an Australian relative of the blue crab—*Scylla serrata*—there can be no doubt. This crab, which may attain an overall span of two feet, does its greatest damage at night. With its powerful claws *Scylla* crushes the shells of the young oysters to get at the meat. Even full-grown oysters are attacked if their growth has been rapid, for the shell is then somewhat weaker or thinner. Crabs of this species are said to make seasonal raids upon the young oysters and may devastate whole beds in a few days' time. Stake fences are employed as a protection against such crab invasions.

In the extensive oyster beds at Matapalo, Peru, another crustacean proves troublesome, this time an isopod. Mangroves are plentiful in this locality, and the trees flourish in soft mud. The oysters, having need of something to which to attach themselves, adhere to the mangroves. But now comes upon the scene the isopod *Sphaeroma peruvianum*, which has a penchant for boring in wood. Entering the stems and roots of the mangroves, it causes the wood to decay. The blighted, honeycombed branches and roots fall away, carrying with them the attached oysters which then disappear in the soft mud below.

Attention has already been called to the better known wood borers—*Limnoria lignorum*, also an isopod, and *Chelura terebrans*, its amphipod associate in crime. Widely distributed and very destructive, these two can wreck untreated or otherwise unprotected harbor installations and piling in a matter of months. There are also other wood-boring isopods, and at least two that bore into stone and concrete harbor works (page 139). The cost of the depredations of these crustaceans must run into millions of dollars. Not to be overlooked are the shipfouling organisms of which barnacles are perhaps the most troublesome. Combating them costs the American shipping industry alone more than a million dollars a year. And not least among the sinners are the parasites, portrayed on so many pages of our Family Album.

These are not all the crustacean sinners, but they are among the worst, and those we know most about. Certainly no one will charge that the evil they do outweighs the good, or that crustacean depredations outbalance the immense contribution of the class to human and animal well-being in general. Our purpose here, however, is not to weigh the Crustacea but to be entertained by them; and if that has been realized, who could ask more—even of a scientist, or a crustacean.

Systematic Index

This classified list indexes by subclasses, superorders, and orders the crustaceans referred to. Technical names are followed, where available, by common (vernacular) names in parentheses, and number of page and figure. Group names for which a page reference is not given are not discussed in the text. The order of names follows the scheme of classification of the Class Crustacea on page 40, where, as here, the subclasses are numbered 1 to 8.

Index

THE UNIVERSITY OF MICHIGAN PRESS